FOR RETURN

Mathematical Theories
of
TRAFFIC FLOW

MATHEMATICS IN
SCIENCE AND ENGINEERING

A Series of Monographs and Textbooks

Edited by

Richard Bellman

The RAND Corporation, Santa Monica, California

Mathematical Theories

of

TRAFFIC FLOW

FRANK A. HAIGHT

Institute of Transportation and Traffic Engineering
University of California
Los Angeles, California

1963

New York   **ACADEMIC PRESS**   London

ACADEMIC PRESS INC.
111 Fifth Avenue, New York 3, New York

United Kingdom Edition published by
ACADEMIC PRESS INC. (LONDON) LTD.
Berkeley Square House, London W.1

Library of Congress Catalog Card Number: 63-15033

PRINTED IN THE UNITED STATES OF AMERICA

Preface

The population of the earth has been persistently increasing throughout recorded history, but only within the twentieth century has its size become an important obstacle to orderly civilization. One of the problems created by this growth, which has proved to be of some mathematical interest, is that of congestion. On land and in the air, in vehicles and on foot, people now get in each others' way to an extent far surpassing that of any previous age. There may have been overcrowding in ancient Rome or Elizabethan London, but it can hardly have constituted the hazard, the inconvenience, or the expense which it does today. We see congestion not only in transportation, but in virtually every aspect of modern life: communication, urban development, commercial organization, reticulation of utilities, mass production, and perhaps even agriculture.

The scientific study of congestion, whether intended to describe or to ameliorate, has been a natural consequence of man's enforced interest in his increasingly overcrowded world. The most fully developed mathematical theory of congestion is *queueing theory*, which deals with accumulation at a fixed point, caused by the need for *service*, and changing with the passage of *time*. The subject is more than fifty years old and is now being extended very vigorously, both in depth of formulation and in breadth of application.

As a source of congestion, the motor vehicle occupies a unique position, both from the practical and from the mathematical point of view. Estimates of the importance of transportation by car are difficult to make, but we can be sure that in an industrialized society the effect is enormous, whether measured economically, politically, in terms of public health, psychologically,* industrially, or purely as a fraction of transportation in general. Some of the central concepts of the present book, such as traffic delay, traffic flow, and traffic density, are popular concepts, and quite justifiably so. Few areas of applied mathematics have such widespread and directly intuitive importance in our lives.

On the mathematical side we find many genuinely interesting aspects of traffic flow. The development in the past decade of a substantial theory of vehicular movement has come not only from the need to understand more exactly the empirical results of the traffic engineering profession, but also as a natural extension of the theory of queues. We consider simultaneously the dimensions of *time* and *space*, and permit delay to arise partially from waiting (sequentially in a single dimension) but more generally from mere proximity in the time-space plane. Many intrinsically attractive mathematical questions arise from the traffic-theoretic formulation, some of which are not yet answered. Although the problems are difficult to formulate and still more difficult to solve, there is by now a considerable literature in traffic flow theory and the subject is ready for systematic exposition.

Perhaps it is unnecessary to add that we are not trying to "solve the traffic problem," any more than a hydrodynamicist is trying to solve the water problem or an entomologist the bug problem. The Traffic Problem, like The Toll of the Road, are expressions quite innocent of precise significance. Our mathematical theories should define, characterize, and describe one specific phenomenon: vehicular traffic. We must assume that these investigations, like those of classical applied mathematics, will lead naturally to improved techniques for practical understanding and control of the subject being studied.

As a simple consequence of its immaturity, traffic flow theory has been developed by research workers of widely varying interests:

---

* A simple anomolous by-product, the traffic accident, engages public attention to an astonishing degree, obscuring industrial and domestic accidents, as well as other more significant contributions to mortality.

mathematicians, physicists, traffic engineers, economists and, more recently, practitioners of operations research. In this circumstance the reader will not be surprised to learn that the field is sprawling, diffuse, and in many ways rather baffling. There is no general agreement on notation or terminology, most of which has been inherited from the traffic engineer. There is very little agreement on methodology, or on which quantities are significant, or on how these quantities should be measured. Armed with the Poisson distribution and a sufficient interest, nearly anyone can find some original, and possibly valuable, theme in traffic flow.

In this, the first attempt to justify the theory as a sensible part of applied mathematics, I have selected fairly ruthlessly from the literature in order to bring out the fundamental relationship between traffic flow theory and the classical subjects of queueing theory, stochastic processes, and mathematical probability. The present volume reflects my belief that the greatest development of traffic theory will take place in these directly connected areas, rather than by analogical variation of equations which apply to other substances.*

It is important to find meaningful middle ground between pure mathematics and traffic engineering. It should be possible to show traffic engineers the usefulness of theoretical analysis, and at the same time the mathematician should find systems worthy of his consideration. Keeping both of these requirements in mind, I use the framework of mathematical demonstration, while dealing with concepts of direct traffic-theoretic significance. A plausible although possibly heuristic, proof is preferred both to empirical dogmatism and to decorative abstraction.

Although I employ the terminology of roads and vehicles, the attentive reader will find many portions of the book with wider application. The postulates of Chapter 3, intended to characterize road traffic, are often partly laid aside, so that the structure is

---

* There are some references to alternatives in the supplementary list which follows Chapter 7. Of these, the "Boltzmann-like" system is the most substantial.

in fact more general. The precise degree of generality varies from section to section, and in a few cases the identification with vehicles is indeed tenuous.

The reader is assumed to have some familiarity with mathematical probability. Chapter 1 is designed as a convenient collection of results for reference, but is self-contained and may be used as a compact introduction to the subject. Chapter 2 stands in the same relation to the theory of queues. No other knowledge is required except for undergraduate mathematics and perhaps an intuitive idea of typical vehicular behavior in industrialized nations.

I owe a great deal to Robert M. Oliver for discussions on traffic flow theory. Chapters 3 and 4 in particular have benefited from our many interesting arguments, and it is a pleasure for me to acknowledge this debt to an esteemed colleague. The manuscript was read by Gordon Newell and Alan Miller, and their comments have been very helpful in preparing the final version. I have also received useful advice and comments from E. Farnsworth Bisbee, Leo Breiman, Leslie Edie, William Jewell, George Weiss, John R. B. Whittlesey, and from the participants in a series of seminars organized by Serge Goldberg of the Ministère des Travaux Publics and given at the Ecole des Ponts et Chausées.

The Institute of Transportation and Traffic Engineering of the University of California has provided me with excellent opportunity for this work, and I am indebted to Professor Harmer Davis and the late Professor J. H. Mathewson for creating an atmosphere so conducive to research. The manuscript was very efficiently typed by Allan S. Jacobson.

I am most particularly grateful to Richard Bellman. He suggested that I write the book and frequently gave me a good clue to some mathematical difficulty.

FRANK A. HAIGHT

February 1963

Contents

Chapter 1

Probability and Statistics

Chapter 2

Theory of Queues

Chapter 3

Fundamental Characteristics of Road Traffic

Chapter 4

Arrangement of Cars on a Road

Chapter 5

The Simple Delay Problem

Chapter 6

Miscellaneous Problems

Chapter 7

A Two Lane Road

CHAPTER **1**

Probability and Statistics

1.1 Introduction

Experiments can be classified into one of two categories, depending on whether their outcomes are certain or uncertain. A *certain experiment* will yield exactly the same value whenever the experiment is repeated under the same conditions; an *uncertain experiment* will give a variety of values. The distinction is pragmatic rather than logical, for many certain experiments can be made uncertain by various methods, particularly refinement of instrumentation. The repeated measurement of length of a line may give the same value if the ruler is coarsely calibrated and several different values if the ruler is more finely calibrated.

Nevertheless, the distinction between certainty and uncertainty is a useful concept, and the mathematical form of the result is quite different. In a certain experiment, the result will consist of a single constant for each quantity measured. The result of an uncertain experiment is called a *random variable*; the study of uncertain results is the science of statistics. A random variable is completely described not by a number but by a function[†] which shows the relative frequency (empirical or theoretical) of occurrence of particular values. The function is called a *statistical distribution*.

Consider the simple experiment of measuring the elapsed time between the arrival of the front bumpers of consecutive cars in a single lane of traffic. If the cars are rigidly scheduled, each value will be exactly the same, and the experiment will not be statistical.

[†] As we shall see there are several functions which are essentially equivalent.

1

However, in an actual traffic situation, many different numbers will be obtained, and these correspond to a statistical distribution. It is an important problem to determine a suitable mathematical function which will accurately describe the relative frequency of different headways, and so characterize the flow of traffic.

If an experiment is uncertain, it is necessary at first to decide what category of results are possible. The region of possibility may form a set of numbers, called the domain of definition for the distribution.

EXAMPLE 1. Number of kittens born in a litter. Domain of definition: 1, 2, 3, 4, ...

EXAMPLE 2. Number of cars counted in a minute of observation. Domain of definition: 0, 1, 2, 3, ...

EXAMPLE 3. Age of an individual. Domain of definition: $(0, \infty)$.

EXAMPLE 4. Number shown on a throw of a die. Domain of definition: 1, 2, 3, 4, 5, 6.

EXAMPLE 5. Spacing between consecutive cars, front bumper to back bumper. Domain of definition: $(0, \infty)$.

EXAMPLE 6. Spacing between consecutive cars, front bumper to front bumper. Domain of definition: (Δ, ∞) where Δ is a car length.

In all the examples given above, with the exception of Example 4, the upper limit is infinite. This may seem wrong in some cases, but it should be remembered that the domain of definition shows possible values, not probable values. In Example 1, values such as -2 or $\frac{1}{2}$ are theoretically impossible but 10, 20, or larger values are simply improbable. It could be argued that by taking a much bigger integer, a truly impossible value could be found. The difficulty in this case is knowing where to truncate. It is more convenient mathematically to adopt the fiction that (perhaps with probability 10^{-1000}) 250 kittens could be born in a litter than to say that it is theoretically possible that 249 could, but theoretically impossible that 250 could. The choice of a convenient domain of definition is perhaps a question of judgment, which can be gradually acquired, as much as a matter of pure logic.

Another aspect of the examples above is the distinction between discrete and continuous domains. In Examples 1, 2, and 4, the only admissible values are positive integers, while in the other cases, a whole range of real values are permitted. This distinction is easier to make than that between finite and infinite domain but even here there may be some doubt. If a measuring instrument is calibrated only in inches, the results it gives would be discrete. As the calibration is improved, the space between possible values decreases, and it is not difficult to see that if there is such a thing as a "true" value, it could be any real positive number.

It turns out that virtually every reasonable experiment which is wholly continuous or wholly discrete will have one of the following domains of definition:

A. The whole real line, $(-\infty, \infty)$. For example, the error in a measurement of length.

B. The positive half of the real line, $(0, \infty)$. For example the age of an individual.

C. A piece of the real line, (a, b). For example, the angle a thrown needle makes with a fixed line on the floor, $a = 0$, $b = \pi$.

D. All the positive integers, beginning with some value, n, $n + 1, n + 2, \ldots$. In Examples 1 and 4, $n = 1$, and in Example 2, $n = 0$.

E. Some of the positive integers. In Example 4, we have just six of the integers possible.

In addition to discrete and continuous domains of definition, there is a third type of domain which is important in road traffic theory: the mixed discrete and continuous. As an example of this, imagine a highway on which all private cars obeyed a speed limit which was given as: minimum 30, maximum 60; and suppose that tractors were allowed to use the road if they traveled at exactly 10 m.p.h. Then the domain of definition would be the continuous interval (30, 60) plus the single value 10.

In the next four sections, we discuss continuous, discrete, and mixed probability distributions, with special emphasis on those important for road traffic.

1.2 Discrete Distributions

Suppose we have some set of the positive integers which are possible outcomes of an experiment. A complete statistical description of that experiment is given when the probability of each outcome is specified. In some cases, such as throwing fair dice, these probabilities can be deduced from the specifications of the experiment. In other cases, such as the birth of kittens, the probabilities can only be determined empirically. Even in the latter cases, however, it is sensible to deal with theoretical values for the probabilities, so that hypothetical functions can be compared with experimental results.

A set of numbers qualifies as probabilities for all the possible results of an experiment provided they are (1) never negative, and (2) add up to unity. Thus the figure zero is taken as the smallest allowable value for a probability, and one as the largest, roughly corresponding to impossibility and certainty.

Let N denote the outcome[†] of the experiment, where $N = 0, 1, 2, \ldots$. Then we write for the probability that N has the value n

$$\text{Prob}\,(N = n) = p_n$$

where $0 \leqslant p_n \leqslant 1$, and $p_0 + p_1 + p_2 + \ldots = 1$.

EXAMPLE 1. Observations on cat life show the table (see facing page) for the frequency of litters of various sizes.

Dividing by 149, we obtain an *empirical* probability distribution for this particular breed of cats (see below table).

[†] It is now standard practice to denote a random variable by a capital letter and the corresponding *dummy variable* in its probability distribution function by the corresponding small letter. In the continuous and mixed cases the letters X, x are frequently used and in the discrete case the letters N, n. However, once in this section (Binomial distribution) and once in the next it will be convenient to call a certain constant N.

Number of kittens	Number of litters
1	3
2	7
3	17
4	25
5	33
6	29
7	20
8	9
9	4
10	2
>10	0
	149

$$p_1 = 3/149 \qquad p_6 = 29/149$$
$$p_2 = 7/149 \qquad p_7 = 20/149$$
$$p_3 = 17/149 \qquad p_8 = 9/149$$
$$p_4 = 25/149 \qquad p_9 = 4/149$$
$$p_5 = 33/149 \qquad p_{10} = 2/149$$
$$p_n = 0, \qquad n > 10.$$

In the remainder of this book, probability distributions will be theoretical, rather than empirical. Let us consider, therefore, some probability distributions which can be found by reasoning, without recourse to trial.

If a fair die is thrown, the probability distribution is $p_1 = p_2 = p_3 = p_4 = p_5 = p_6 = 1/6$. How is this known? It might be mistakenly assumed that the values 1/6 could only be determined by experiment. Actually, the situation is quite the reverse. The list of six 1/6's is in fact the *definition* of a *fair* die. The statistical problem then becomes one of deciding whether or not any particular die is fair.

Any convergent series of positive constants can be used to form a probability distribution. We define three of these which are of importance in road traffic theory, and then show the types of traffic experiments which yield these distributions.

GEOMETRIC DISTRIBUTION. Consider the geometric series

$$1 + \rho + \rho^2 + \rho^3 + \dots .$$

If $\rho < 1$, this is a convergent series, and has the sum $1/(1 - \rho)$. Therefore, a valid probability distribution can be defined simply by multiplying each term of the series by $(1 - \rho)$, as follows:

$$p_0 = (1 - \rho)$$
$$p_1 = (1 - \rho)\,\rho \qquad\qquad (1)$$
$$p_2 = (1 - \rho)\,\rho^2$$

with the general expression $p_n = (1 - \rho)\rho^n$, $n = 0, 1, 2, \dots$. In Chapter 2, we shall see that an important quantity, the length of a queue, has this distribution.

POISSON DISTRIBUTION. Consider the exponential series

$$1 + \lambda + \lambda^2/2! + \lambda^3/3! + \dots ,$$

which is convergent for all λ, and has the sum e^λ. Dividing by e^λ, we obtain a valid probability distribution, defined as follows:

$$p_0 = e^{-\lambda}$$
$$p_1 = \lambda\,e^{-\lambda} \qquad\qquad (2)$$
$$p_2 = \lambda^2\,e^{-\lambda}/2!$$

with the general expression $p_n = \lambda^n\,e^{-\lambda}/n!$, $n = 0, 1, 2, \dots$. This distribution, as we shall prove later, describes the probability that exactly n randomly[†] arranged cars will be observed in unit length of road.

[†] The word *random* is used in two ways in statistics: (a) as the equivalent of *uncertain*, and (b) as the equivalent of *Poisson*. In this book it will always have the second meaning, except when speaking of a *random variable*.

BINOMIAL DISTRIBUTION. Suppose we choose two numbers which add up to unity, say $p + q = 1$. Expand $(p + q)^N$ in a binomial series, where N is a fixed integer, and obtain

$$p^N + Np^{N-1}q + \binom{N}{2}p^{N-2}q^2 + \binom{N}{3}p^{N-3}q^3 + \cdots +$$

$$pq^{N-1} + q^N = 1.$$

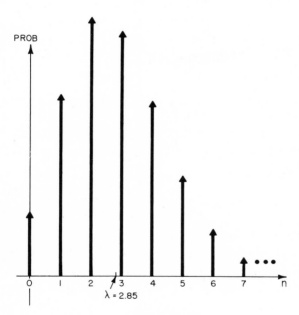

FIG. 1. A discrete distribution.

Therefore, a valid probability distribution can be defined as

$$p_n = \binom{N}{n}p^{N-n}q^n, \qquad n = 0, 1, \ldots, N.$$

Notice that for this distribution, the domain of definition consists of only $N + 1$ values.

It is possible to represent a discrete probability distribution geometrically by erecting an ordinate of length p_n over each value n. Figure 1 shows a typical form for the Poisson distribution.

1.3 Random Points on a Line

A Bernoulli experiment is an experiment which has only two possible outcomes, with constant probabilities p and $q = 1 - p$; for example, the flipping of a coin. For convenience, the two outcomes are called "success" and "failure." If a Bernoulli experiment is performed N times in succession, the probability of exactly n successes $(n = 0, 1, \ldots, N)$ is the binomial distribution.

Proof. The probability of getting first n successes is p^n, and then $N - n$ failures is q^{N-n}; therefore, the probability of n successes followed by $N - n$ failures is $p^n q^{N-n}$. But a total of n successes may be arranged by permuting the above sequence in any one of the $\binom{N}{n}$ possible ways, leading to the binomial expression.

EXAMPLE. A fair coin is tossed 50 times. What is the probability of exactly 25 heads? $p = q = \frac{1}{2}$, since the coin is fair, $N = 50$, $n = 25$, and therefore

$$\text{Prob (25 heads)} = p_{25} = \binom{50}{25}\left(\frac{1}{2}\right)^{25}\left(\frac{1}{2}\right)^{25}.$$

Now suppose that points are dropped at random on an infinitely long line in such a way that the average number of points per unit length is λ. Then the probability of finding exactly n points on a finite segment of length τ is the Poisson probability with λ replaced by $\lambda\tau$.

Proof. Take a finite segment of length t which completely surrounds τ. In dropping each of N points, we have a Bernoulli experiment in which the probability of a success (falling on τ) is τ/t, and the probability of failure (falling on t but outside τ) is $1 - \tau/t$. Therefore, by the previous result, the probability of obtaining exactly n points in τ is

$$p_n = \binom{N}{n}(\tau/t)^n (1 - \tau/t)^{N-n}, \qquad n = 0, 1, 2, \ldots, N.$$

Let t approach infinity, and N approach infinity in such a way that N/t approaches the constant density of points λ.

$$p_n = \frac{1}{n!} \left[N(N-1)(N-2) \ldots (N-n+1) \right] \times$$

$$\left(\frac{N}{t}\right)^n \left(\frac{\tau}{N}\right)^n \left(1 - \frac{N}{t}\frac{\tau}{N}\right)^{N-n}$$

$$= \frac{\tau^n}{n!} \left[1\left(1 - \frac{1}{N}\right)\left(1 - \frac{2}{N}\right) \ldots \left(1 - \frac{N-n+1}{N}\right) \right] \times$$

$$\left(\frac{N}{t}\right)^n \left(1 - \frac{N}{t}\frac{\tau}{N}\right)^{N-n}$$

and in the limit described above, this approaches

$$\frac{\tau^n}{n!} \lambda^n e^{-\lambda\tau} \tag{1}$$

by virtue of the well known exponential limit

$$e^x = \lim_{N \to \infty} \left(1 + \frac{x}{N}\right)^N$$

In case the counting period τ is taken as a unit of length, Eq. (1) becomes exactly the Poisson distribution as defined by Eq. (2) of Section 1.2.

We have used the letters t and τ in this proof to be suggestive of a time axis, and the counts of random points might be supposed to be taken with respect to time. If vehicular counts by means of a road tape corresponded reasonably well to the Poisson distribution, the moments of arrivals could therefore be considered random. Alternatively, the axis might be space, and the points be cars as recorded by an aerial photograph.

1.4 Continuous Distributions

When the domain of definition is all or part of the real line, the representation of probabilities by a list (possibly infinite) as in the preceding section breaks down. We use instead a continuous single valued function to indicate how probable the various out-

comes of the experiment are. The integral between any two limits
gives the probability of a result between those values:

$$\text{Prob} \ (a < \text{result} < b) = \int_a^b f(x) \, dx \qquad (1)$$

where $f(x)$ is a function (called the density function) corresponding
to the discrete p_n. The function should be always positive, and
have total area unity. When the function is not specified, it is
convenient to use the limits $(-\infty, \infty)$, with the understanding that
if the domain is less than the whole real line, $f(x)$ is defined to be
identically zero outside its meaningful domain. Therefore, for a
function $f(x)$ to be a density, we require

$$f(x) \geqslant 0, \qquad \text{and} \qquad \int_{-\infty}^{\infty} f(x) \, dx = 1. \qquad (2)$$

It is only a matter of tradition to use the functional notation with
variable x in the continuous case and the subscript notation with
variable n in the discrete case; these might equally well be written
$p(n)$, or f_x.

In looking for functions suitable to be made into density functions, we want first of all finite area, just as we wanted convergent
discrete series. Then the area can be divided into the function,
so that Eq. (2) will be satisfied. As examples, we choose three
which have applications to road traffic. In succeeding chapters,
several other special continuous distributions will be mentioned.

TYPE III DISTRIBUTION. This name is a remnant of a classification system for distributions proposed by Karl Pearson.
The distribution is defined over the positive real line, and is based
on the function $e^{-\lambda x} x^{k-1}$, where λ and k are two positive constants.
It begins at the origin, goes up to a maximum, and is then
asymptotic to the axis. By suitable choice of λ and k, the shape
can be changed considerably, and Type III distributions will fit
many kinds of essentially positive data. The area contained under

the curve, which must be divided out to produce unit area, involves the gamma function:

$$\Gamma(z) = \int_0^\infty e^{-t}\, t^{z-1}\, dt. \tag{3}$$

Integrating Eq. (3) by parts once shows that

$$\Gamma(z) = (z-1)\,\Gamma(z-1), \tag{4}$$

and repeated integration by parts yields, in case z is integral

$$\Gamma(z) = (z-1)!. \tag{5}$$

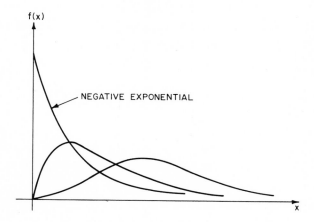

FIG. 2. Continuous distributions.

Using Eq. (3), it is easy to see that the area under $e^{-\lambda x}\, x^{k-1}$ is $\Gamma(k)/k^\lambda$, and therefore the Type III density function is

$$f(x) = \frac{\lambda^k}{\Gamma(k)}\, e^{-\lambda x}\, x^{k-1}, \qquad 0 < x < \infty. \tag{6}$$

Figure 2 shows several typical Type III densities. An important special case (in which $k = 1$) is the following.

NEGATIVE EXPONENTIAL DISTRIBUTION.

$$\lambda e^{-\lambda x}, \qquad 0 < x < \infty. \tag{7}$$

If points occur at random on a line, so that the probability of n points in unit length is Poisson, the distribution of lengths of gaps between consecutive points has the density (7), and conversely. The proof of this important fact will be given in several different ways in the succeeding sections. The relationship, in which the general idea of randomness of points is characterized in either one of two ways will have significance in several other contexts, and therefore is given a special name. For random points, the *counting* distribution is the Poisson, and the *gap* distribution is the negative exponential. Later, the general relationship between counting and gap distributions for nonrandom arrangements of points will be studied. In traffic theory, randomness is not always a suitable assumption.

TYPE I DISTRIBUTION. We begin with the function $x^{p-1}(1-x)^{q-1}$, defined over the unit interval $(0, 1)$. In order to determine the correct constant to multiply this function by, write

$$\Gamma(p)\,\Gamma(q) = \int_0^\infty e^{-t}\,t^{p-1}\,dt \int_0^\infty e^{-s}\,s^{q-1}\,ds$$

$$= \int_0^\infty \int_0^\infty e^{-s-t}\,t^{p-1}\,s^{q-1}\,dt\,ds$$

and use the transformation

$$u = \frac{t}{s+t}, \qquad v = s+t.$$

This is equivalent to

$$t = vu, \qquad s = v - vu$$

with Jacobian $= v$. The range of u is now $(0, 1)$ and of v is $(0, \infty)$. Hence

$$\Gamma(p)\,\Gamma(q) = \int_0^1 \int_0^\infty e^{-vu}\,(vu)^{p-1}\,e^{-v(1-u)}\,v^{q-1}\,(1-u)^{q-1}\,v\,du\,dv,$$

$$= \Gamma(p+q) \int_0^1 u^{p-1}\,(1-u)^{q-1}\,du$$

and therefore the correct constant is $\Gamma(p+q)/\Gamma(p)\Gamma(q)$. The beta function of p and q is defined by

$$B(p, q) = \frac{\Gamma(p)\,\Gamma(q)}{\Gamma(p+q)}. \tag{8}$$

Hence, the Type I density function can be written

$$\frac{x^{p-1}(1-x)^{q-1}}{B(p,q)}, \qquad 0 < x < 1. \tag{9}$$

1.5 Mixed Distributions

Consider the example of cars and tractors given in Section 1.1, and suppose the proportion of cars to be α and of tractors to be $1-\alpha$. Further, suppose the Type I distribution would provide a good fit for the speeds of cars, for some p and q, provided it covered the right interval $(30, 60)$ instead of $(0, 1)$ as in formula (9) of Section 1.4. What is the correct distribution for all speeds of vehicles? The height of the discrete component, or "spike" should be $1-\alpha$, and this spike should be placed at the point 10. The area of the continuous component (density) should be α, and should be made to cover $(30, 60)$. In other words, we need to (i) extend the range of Eq. (9) to 30 units, (ii) translate 30 units away from the origin, and (iii) reduce the area from 1 to α. We accomplish this in three steps. First, let $y = 30\,x$. In order to preserve the unit integral, it is necessary to multiply by 30, since $dy = 30\,dx$.[†]

Therefore, the density of y is

$$\frac{30\,(y/30)^{p-1}(1-y/30)^{q-1}}{B(p,q)}.$$

Next, use the translation $z = y + 30$, and multiply by the constant α. A modified Type I density for the continuous component is thus

---

[†] A better theoretical explanation of this maneuver will be given in Section 1.6.

$$30\alpha\frac{\left[\dfrac{z-30}{30}\right]^{p-1}\left[1-\dfrac{z-30}{30}\right]^{q-1}}{\mathrm{B}(p,q)}. \tag{1}$$

This component can be combined with the spike to give a single distribution by using the function

$$\delta(z) = \begin{cases} 1, & z = 0 \\ 0, & z \neq 0 \end{cases} \tag{2}$$

The speed distribution for this artificial example is (see Fig. 3)

$$(1-\alpha)\,\delta(x-10) + \text{formula (1)}. \tag{3}$$

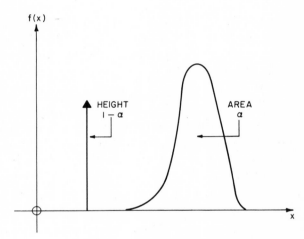

Fig. 3. A mixed distribution.

A more realistic mixed distribution arises from the hypothesis that cars may form waiting lines or queues when they are unable to pass a slow moving car on the highway. Then the spike in the distribution of gap size will be at the point of separation of consecutive cars. Another important mixed distribution applies to the waiting time in an ordinary queue; in this case there is a spike at the origin, corresponding to those individuals who arrive when the queue is empty, and so do not have to wait at all, and a continuous component defined over $(0, \infty)$, corresponding to the waiting times of customers actually delayed. Other, more complicated possibilities, involving several spikes, can be defined theoretically, but will not be used in this book.

In working with mixed distributions, it is necessary to use a mixture of summation and integration. For example, Eq. (3) above has unit sum-area, sum being on the first term and area of the second.[†]

1.6 Cumulative Distributions

The subdivision between discrete and continuous distributions is perfectly natural because of the nature of experimental results, but it is mathematically troublesome. These difficulties are only partially illustrated by the mixed distributions. Further problems will arise in manipulation of distributions to find some of their properties, for an integral sign will be used in the continuous case and a summation sign in the discrete case. A good theoretical way of getting around this is by use of the Stieltjes integral, but for some purposes, the cumulative distribution is more satisfactory. If $f(x)$ is a continuous density, the corresponding cumulative distribution is defined by

$$F(x) = \int_{-\infty}^{x} f(t)\, dt,$$

where the lower limit of integration is, as usual, adjusted to the lower value of the domain of definition. In terms of $F(x)$, it is possible to relate random variables X (outcomes of an experiment) directly with a mathematical function without using the superfluous constants a and b of formula (1), Section 1.4:

$$\text{Prob } (X \leqslant x) = F(x), \tag{1}$$

[†] If one wishes to avoid this slight impurity, one can do so by defining $\delta(z)$ not as in (2) above, but as $\delta(z) = \infty$ when $z = 0$, such that $\int_{-\infty}^{\infty} \delta(z)\, dz = 1$. On the whole, it seems easier to sum and integrate in the same equation according to easy rules.

where $F(-\infty) = 0$, $F(\infty) = 1$. Also, $f(x)$ can be obtained by simple differentiation,

$$f(x) = \frac{d}{dx} F(x).$$

Using the cumulative function yields a simple rule for finding the density of a transformed variable. Suppose that X has distribution $f(x)$; what is the distribution of $Z = \phi(X)$? Let the cumulative distribution for Z be $G(z)$, with $(d/dz)G(z) = g(z)$. Then

$$F(x) = \text{Prob}\,(X \leqslant x)$$
$$= \text{Prob}\,(\phi^{-1}(Z) \leqslant x)$$
$$= \text{Prob}\,(Z \leqslant \phi(x)),$$

and therefore,

$$F(\phi^{-1}(x)) = \text{Prob}\,(Z \leqslant x) = G(x).$$

Differentiating,

$$g(x) = f(\phi^{-1}(x)) \frac{d}{dx} \phi^{-1}(x). \tag{2}$$

This means that to find the density for a transformed[†] variable, it is only necessary to substitute and multiply by the derivative of the inverse transformation. In the mixed distribution example of Section 1.5, the appropriate multiplier is

$$\frac{d}{dx} \phi^{-1}(x) = \frac{d}{dx} 30\, x = 30;$$

hence, the factor 30.

Strictly correct notation requires a different letter for the random variable and for the argument of the distribution. This is frequently inconvenient in practice, and the shorter form "a variable x has distribution $f(x)$" is often used. In doing so, it is important to remember that *each transformation of a continuous*

---

† Where the inverse exists and is differentiable.

density must be performed as though the differential dx were present.
The rule in italics is equivalent to formula (2).

Whenever a spike occurs, the cumulative distribution jumps up by the length of the spike; in other words discrete components correspond to discontinuities in $F(x)$. If $F(x)$ is always continuous, the distribution is a continuous one; if $F(x)$ is a step function, the distribution is discrete. The cumulative function corresponding to Fig. 3 is shown in Fig. 4.

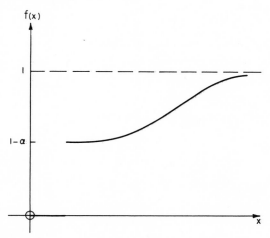

FIG. 4. A cumulative distribution for the mixed case.

Cumulative functions are valuable theoretically, but for particular distributions they may be very cumbersome.

GEOMETRIC DISTRIBUTION

$$P_n = \sum_{i=0}^{n} (1 - \rho)\, \rho^i = 1 - \rho^{n+1}. \tag{3}$$

POISSON DISTRIBUTION

$$P_n = \sum_{i=0}^{n} \frac{e^{-\lambda}\, \lambda^i}{i!} \tag{4}$$

which has no simple form.

BINOMIAL DISTRIBUTION

$$P_n = \sum_{i=0}^{n} \binom{N}{i} p^i (1-p)^{N-i} \tag{5}$$

which has no simple form.

TYPE III DISTRIBUTION

$$F(x) = \int_0^x \frac{\lambda^k}{\Gamma(k)} e^{-\lambda t} t^{k-1} dt. \tag{6}$$

Although this function has no simple form, it occurs often enough in applied mathematics to deserve a special name and symbol. The function

$$\gamma(n, x) = \int_0^x e^{-t} t^{n-1} dt \tag{7}$$

is called the incomplete gamma function; in these terms, (6) may be written

$$\frac{\gamma(k, \lambda x)}{\Gamma(k)}. \tag{8}$$

The upper part of the gamma integral is denoted by $\Gamma(n, x)$ so that

$$\gamma(n, x) + \Gamma(n, x) = \Gamma(n). \tag{9}$$

It is possible to express the cumulative Poisson distribution in terms of $\Gamma(n, x)$:

$$\sum_{i=0}^{n} \frac{e^{-\lambda} \lambda^i}{i!} = \frac{\Gamma(n+1, \lambda)}{\Gamma(n+1)}. \tag{10}$$

A proof of this rather surprising fact may be obtained by repeated integration by parts of $\Gamma(n+1, \lambda)$ for integral n.

TYPE I DISTRIBUTION.

$$F(x) = \int_0^x \frac{t^{p-1}(1-t)^{q-1}}{B(p, q)} dt.$$

This cumulative distribution defines the incomplete beta function, as follows:

$$F(x) = \frac{B(p, q, x)}{B(p, q)}.$$

Because of their close connection with the gamma and beta functions respectively, the Type III distribution is also called the gamma distribution, and the Type I distribution is also called the beta distribution.

Just as the cumulative Poisson probabilities can be expressed in terms of the incomplete gamma function, so the cumulative binomial probabilities can be expressed in terms of the incomplete beta function. The sum given by Eq. (5) can also be written

$$\sum_{i=0}^{n} \binom{N}{i} p^i (1-p)^{N-i} = 1 - \frac{B(n+1, N-n, p)}{B(n+1, N-n)}. \quad (11)$$

We shall now prove that random points (Poisson counting distribution) implies negative exponential gap distribution.

Suppose the counting distribution is Poisson, and let

$$F(x) = \text{Prob (gap} \leqslant x) = 1 - \text{Prob (gap} > x)$$

$$= 1 - \text{Prob (no points in an interval of length } x) \quad (12)$$

$$= 1 - e^{-\lambda x},$$

which is the cumulative form of the negative exponential distribution. The converse of this theorem will be proven in a later section.

1.7 Moments and Expectation

All the distributions which we have mentioned contain certain parameters, and are really therefore families of distributions:

Geometric	ρ
Poisson	λ
Binomial	N, p

Type III λ, k

Negative Exponential λ

Type I p, q

To show how these quantities are related to the probabilistic properties of the distributions, and consequently to the experiments which are being described, we define several standard quantities which apply to all of these distributions:

$$k\text{th moment about the origin} = m_k = \int x^k f(x) \, dx \qquad (1)$$

$$= \sum n^k p_n,$$

$$k\text{th moment about the mean} = \int (x - m_1)^k f(x) \, dx \qquad (2)$$

$$= \sum (n - m_1)^k p_n,$$

where all integrals and sums are taken over the appropriate domains of definition. Two of these moments are of particular interest:

$$\text{arithmetic mean} = m_1 = m = \int x f(x) \, dx = \sum n p_n \qquad (3)$$

$$\text{variance} = v = \int (x - m)^2 f(x) \, dx = \sum (n - m)^2 p_n. \qquad (4)$$

Simple calculations relate the parameters to the mean and variance:

GEOMETRIC $\qquad\qquad\quad m = \rho (1 - \rho)^{-1}, \quad v = \rho (1 - \rho)^{-2} \qquad (5)$

POISSON $\qquad\qquad\qquad\quad m = v = \lambda \qquad\qquad\qquad\qquad\qquad\quad (6)$

BINOMIAL $\qquad\qquad\qquad m = N p, \qquad\qquad v = N p (1 - p) \qquad (7)$

TYPE III $\qquad\qquad\qquad\quad m = k/\lambda, \qquad\qquad v = k/\lambda^2 \qquad\qquad (8)$

NEGATIVE EXPONENTIAL $m = 1/\lambda, \qquad\qquad\quad v = 1/\lambda^2 \qquad\qquad (9)$

TYPE I $\quad m = p (p + q)^{-1}, \quad v = p q (p + q)^{-2}(p + q + 1)^{-1}. \quad (10)$

These values, as well as higher moments, can be calculated by direct application of formulas (1)–(4). The mean and variance are sometimes valuable in making a preliminary estimate of the appropriateness of a particular distribution. For example, if data yielded a mean and variance which were substantially unequal, the Poisson distribution would not be chosen to represent this data.

The variance is an always positive quantity which measures the average squared distance of an observation from the mean. Consequently, $v = 0$ means that all the probability is concentrated in a unit spike at the mean value. Such a distribution is called *deterministic*, and describes a *certain* experiment in which only one result is possible. The distinction between certain and uncertain experiments — between deterministic and probabilistic phenomena — is therefore expressible as $v = 0$, $v \neq 0$.

The calculation of moments typically involves very similar integrals and sums, in which only the multiplier of $f(x)$ or p_n is altered. To simplify notation, the letter E is used as follows:

$$E(\phi(x)) = \int \phi(x) \, f(x) \, dx$$

$$E(\phi(n)) = \sum \phi(n) \, p_n,$$

and $E(\phi)$ is called the mathematical expectation of the function ϕ (with respect to some particular distribution). Thus $E(x)$ is the arithmetic mean.

Although this notation is extremely convenient for certain types of calculations, it can be confusing at first, for $E(x)$ is not a function of x. On the contrary, it is a parameter of the distribution rather than a function of the random variable. A simple example of the compactness provided by expectation symbols is obtained by expressing the central moments in terms of the moments about the mean:

$$E(x - m) = E(x) - E(m) = m - m = 0$$
$$v = E(x - m)^2 = E(x^2) - 2m \, E(x) + m^2 = E(x^2) - m^2$$
$$= m_2 - m^2 \tag{11}$$

$$E(x-m)^3 = E(x^3) - 3m\,E(x^2) + 3m^3 - m^3 = m_3 - 3m\,m_2 + 2m^3,$$

etc.

Another parameter of interest in traffic flow theory is the harmonic mean, defined by

$$\text{H. M.} = \frac{1}{E(1/x)} \qquad (12)$$

The reason for using the harmonic mean in some circumstances will be discussed fully later, but a simple example will show the difficulties which arise with collections of vehicles. Suppose three cars travel five miles each, at speeds 25, 30, and 50, respectively. Their mean speed is clearly 35 m.p.h. Similarly, the mean elapsed time is 28/60 hours. However, these three values (5 miles, 35 m.p.h. and 28/60 hours) do not satisfy the equation

$$\text{(distance)} = \text{(rate)(time)} \qquad (13)$$

The reason is that Eq. (13) is valid for mean values only if the harmonic mean is used for the rate and the arithmetic mean for the time, or conversely. We return to this question in Section 4.6.

The arithmetic mean is related in a very simple way to the cumulative distribution. Defining $G(x) = 1 - F(x)$, integration by parts shows that

$$m = \int_0^\infty G(x)\,dx \qquad (14)$$

for the continuous case. Similarly

$$m = \sum_{n=0}^\infty Q_n \qquad (15)$$

in the discrete case, where $Q_n = 1 - P_n$. $G(x)$ and Q_n are called the *tails* of the distributions.

1.8 Bivariate Distributions

When an uncertain experiment is performed, more than one variable may be obtained.

EXAMPLE 1. Birth of kittens. $n =$ number of kittens, $x =$ age of mother.

EXAMPLE 2. Counting cars. $n =$ number of cars counted in one minute, $x =$ mean speed of cars counted.

EXAMPLE 3. $x =$ age of an individual, $y =$ weight of same individual.

EXAMPLE 4. $n =$ number shown on top in a throw of a die, $N =$ number shown on nearest side.

EXAMPLE 5. $x =$ space between consecutive cars, $n =$ number of passengers in leading car.

EXAMPLE 6. $x =$ space between consecutive cars, $y =$ relative speeds of two cars.

The domains of definition above, and the corresponding probability distributions, are *bivariate*. Examples 3 and 6 are continuous both ways; Example 4 is discrete both ways; Examples 1, 2, and 5 are discrete one way and continuous the other. To avoid notational difficulties, we will use $f(x, y)$ in all cases. By definition, $f(x, y) \geqslant 0$, and

$$\iint f(x, y) \, dx \, dy = 1,$$

where the domain of integration (or summation) is determined from the experiment. Furthermore, each bivariate density can be reduced to a single variate density in two ways:

$$g(x) = \int f(x, y) \, dy \qquad \text{and} \qquad h(y) = \int f(x, y) \, dx.$$

The densities $g(x)$ and $h(y)$ are called *marginal totals* in applied statistics, and *unconditional distributions* in theoretical statistics. They represent the distributions which would have been obtained if only one or the other variable had been observed in the first place. The ratio $f(x, y)/g(x)$ is a valid density function for y, and is called the *array distribution* for fixed x in applied statistics, and the *conditional distribution* in theoretical statistics. It is indicated by the symbol

$$j(y|x) = \frac{f(x, y)}{g(x)} \tag{1}$$

and can be thought of as the density of y for a fixed value of x. Similarly, we define

$$k(x|y) = \frac{f(x, y)}{h(y)}. \tag{2}$$

For instance, in Example 1, $j(x|6)$ would be the mother's age distribution, computed only for those mothers having a litter of six. These five densities for the bivariate case become much more numerous if there are three or more variables, and it is a problem to devise notation to keep up with the number of densities. A very convenient device is to use square brackets around a set of variables for the density of that set. With three variables, x, y, and z, we could write

$$[x, y, z] = [x|y, z]\,[y, z] = [x, y|z]\,[z]$$
$$= [y|x, z]\,[x, z] = [x, z|y]\,[y]$$
$$= [z|x, y]\,[x, y] = [y, z|x]\,[x]$$

the rule being that (a) each bracket is a density only in those variables preceding the vertical bar, and (b) when a vertical bar is introduced, all variables following it must be written again in their own bracket. The bivariate case

$$[x, y] = [x|y]\,[y] = [y|x]\,[x] \tag{3}$$

is called Bayes Theorem. The quantities following the vertical bar are very similar to parameters. For example, consider the negative exponential distribution with parameter λ. In some circumstances, λ itself might be a random variable, so that

$$\lambda\,e^{-\lambda x} = [x|\lambda]. \tag{4}$$

If the unconditional distribution of λ was also negative exponential with parameter μ

$$[\lambda] = \mu\, e^{-\mu\lambda}$$

then the unconditional distribution of x could be found by integrating λ out of Eq. (3)

$$[x] = \int [x,\, \lambda]\, d\lambda = \int [x|\lambda]\, [\lambda]\, d\lambda$$

$$= \int_0^\infty \lambda\, e^{-\lambda x}\, \mu\, e^{-\lambda\mu}\, d\lambda \tag{5}$$

$$= \frac{\mu}{(x + \mu)^2}.$$

The density (5) is called the Cauchy distribution, and is remarkable in that it has no moments.

The procedure employed in this example can be regarded as averaging the conditional distribution $[x|\lambda]$ over the weights for λ. Although we will have many occasions to perform such calculations, we will not use the square bracket notation, and now return to the more traditional forms of Eqs. (1) and (2).

In case $j(y|x) = h(y)$, the density of y is independent of values of x, and $k(x|y) = g(x)$ also, since

$$f(x, y) = g(x)\, h(y). \tag{6}$$

Equation (6) defines *independent*[†] random variables. In the examples given above, only Example 5 defines variables which one would suppose to be independent. In the first proof of Section 1.3, the independence of the Bernoulli trials was tacitly assumed in stating that the probability of n consecutive successes was p^n if the probability of a single success was p.

[†] Equation (6) is a necessary condition for independence. For sufficiency, we must also assume that the domain of definition of x (or y) does not depend on y (or x).

The important bivariate moments are

$$m_x = E(x) = \int x\, g(x)\, dx = \iint x\, f(x, y)\, dx\, dy$$

$$m_y = E(y) = \int y\, h(y)\, dy = \iint y\, f(x, y)\, dx\, dy$$

$$v_x = E(x - m_x)^2 = \iint (x - m_x)^2\, f(x, y)\, dx\, dy$$

$$v_y = E(y - m_y)^2 = \iint (y - m_y)^2\, f(x, y)\, dx\, dy$$

$$\mathrm{cov}(x, y) = E(x - m_x)(y - m_y) = \iint (x - m_x)(y - m_y)\, f(x, y)\, dx\, dy.$$

The second moment $\mathrm{cov}(x, y)$ is called the *covariance* and

$$r_{xy} = \frac{\mathrm{cov}(x, y)}{\sqrt{v_x\, v_y}}$$

is called the *correlation coefficient*.

1.9 Auxiliary Functions

We have seen that a single variable probability distribution can be characterized by either of the two functions $f(x)$ or $F(x)$, and it must be obvious that many other functions can be defined by transformations, which, provided they are unique, will characterize the distribution equally well.

MOMENT GENERATING FUNCTION: $\phi(s) = E(e^{sx})$. This function has the property that its power series expansion involves m_n as coefficients.

$$\phi(s) = E(e^{sx}) = \int e^{sx}\, f(x)\, dx$$

$$= \int \sum \frac{(sx)^n}{n!}\, f(x)\, dx$$

$$= \sum \frac{s^n}{n!} \int x^n f(x)\, dx \qquad (1)$$

$$= \sum \frac{s^n}{n!}\, m_n.$$

LAPLACE TRANSFORMATION: $\phi(-s)$.

MELLIN TRANSFORMATION: $E(x^{n-1}) = m_{n-1}$.

PROBABILITY GENERATING FUNCTION: $\pi(s) = \sum p_n s^n$.

EXPONENTIAL PROBABILITY GENERATING FUNCTION:

$\sigma(s) = \sum p_n s^n/n!$. It is not difficult to see that

$$\pi(s) = \int_0^\infty e^{-t}\, \sigma(ts)\, dt$$

and therefore, that $\sigma(s)$ is the inverse Laplace transform of $(1/s)\, \pi\, (1/s)$. The successive derivatives of $\pi(s)$, evaluated at $s = 1$, are called the *factorial moments*, and are easy to express in terms of the m_n. For example,

$$\pi'(1) = \sum n\, p_n = m$$

$$\pi''(1) = \sum n\, (n-1)\, p_n = m_2 - m = v + m^2 - m \qquad (2)$$

$$\pi'''(1) = \sum n\, (n-1)(n-2)\, p_n = m_3 - 3m_2 + 2m,$$

and so forth.

There is a particularly simple relationship between the Laplace transform of a density and the Laplace transform of the corresponding cumulative distribution function. If

$$F(x) = \int_0^x f(t)\, dt,$$

(taking the domain to be positive, as it will be in subsequent applications) and we integrate

$$\phi(s) = \int_0^\infty e^{-sx} f(x) \, dx \tag{3}$$

by parts, we obtain

$$\phi(s) = e^{-sx} F(x)\big|_0^\infty + \int_0^\infty s \, e^{-sx} F(x) \, dx$$

which can be written

$$\Phi(s) = \phi(s)/s, \tag{4}$$

where $\Phi(s)$ is the Laplace transform of $F(x)$, defined by

$$\Phi(s) = \int_0^\infty e^{-sx} F(x) \, dx.$$

1.10 Distribution of Independent Sums

Suppose three cars are traveling in a single lane in such a way that the distribution of the gap x between car one and car two is $f(x)$, and the distribution of the gap y between car two and car three is $g(y)$. What is the distribution of the distance $x + y$ between cars one and three, assuming x and y to be independent? The variable itself is the sum of two variables, but it would be a mistake to suppose that the distribution of the sum is the sum of the distributions. In fact, the sum of two densities is not even a density, since the area is no longer one. Let the cumulative distributions of f and g be F and G, and let $z = x + y$ have density h and cumulative distribution H. Then

$$H(u) = \text{Prob} \, (z \leqslant u) = \text{Prob} \, (x + y \leqslant u).$$

The inequality $x + y \leqslant u$ defines the area below the line $x + y = u$ in the (x, y) plane, and therefore

$$H(u) = \int_0^\infty \int_0^{u-y} f(x)\, g(y)\, dx\, dy \tag{1}$$

$$= \int_0^\infty F(u-y)\, g(y)\, dy.$$

Differentiating with respect to u,

$$h(u) = \int_0^\infty f(u-y)\, g(y)\, dy$$

but since $f(u-y)$ vanishes whenever y exceeds u,

$$h(u) = \int_0^u f(u-y)\, g(y)\, dy \tag{2}$$

The function h is called the *convolution* of the functions f and g, and it is clearly unchanged if formula (2) is written

$$h(u) = \int_0^u f(y)\, g(u-y)\, dy.$$

The convolution relationship is expressed symbolically by an asterisk:

$$h = f*g$$

or, if f and g are the same function,

$$f*f = f^{2*}$$
$$f*(f*f) = f^{3*}$$

and so forth. The limits of integration for convolutions may be different from those chosen in the above argument which assumed non-negative variables. We apply the convolution theorem to randomly arranged cars, and find that if individual gaps are distributed with density

$$\lambda\, e^{-\lambda x}$$

then double gaps are distributed with density

$$\int_0^x \lambda\, e^{-\lambda t}\, \lambda\, e^{-\lambda(x-t)}\, dt = \lambda^2\, x\, e^{-\lambda x}$$

Extending this by mathematical induction to the sum of k negative exponential gaps, we obtain a Type III density with parameters k and λ. That is

$$(\lambda\, e^{-\lambda x})^{k*} = \frac{\lambda^k}{\Gamma(k)}\, e^{-\lambda x}\, x^{k-1}. \tag{3}$$

Next, we show that the Laplace transform[†] of the distribution of a sum is the product of the individual Laplace transforms. Suppose the transforms of $f(x)$ and $g(y)$ are $\alpha(s)$ and $\beta(s)$, so that (since x and y are independent)

$$\int_0^\infty \int_0^\infty f(u-y)\, g(y)\, e^{-su}\, du\, dy$$

$$= \int_0^\infty \int_0^u f(u-y)\, g(y)\, e^{-su}\, dy\, du$$

which is the Laplace transform of Eq. (2).

If we compute the Laplace transform of the Type III distribution, obtaining

$$\left(\frac{\lambda}{\lambda + s}\right)^k, \tag{4}$$

the mere fact that this is the kth power of the negative exponential Laplace transform $\lambda\,(\lambda + s)^{-1}$ proves Eq. (3).

Now it is possible to show that negative exponential gaps must yield a Poisson counting distribution. Let

$$p_n(t) = \text{Prob } (n \text{ cars in time } t), \qquad n = 0, 1, 2, \ldots$$

---

† The same result is true for the generating function.

have the cumulative form

$$P_n(t) = \text{Prob} \ (\leqslant n \text{ cars in time } t), \qquad n = 0, 1, 2, \dots .$$

Then

$$\text{Prob (number of cars in } t \text{ is} < n) = \text{Prob (sum of } n \text{ gaps} \geqslant t)$$

which means that

$$P_{n-1}(t) = \int_t^\infty f^{n*}(x)\, dx \tag{5}$$

where $f(x)$ is the gap distribution. In case the gaps are negative exponential, Eq. (3) shows that the convolution is Type III, and therefore, Eq. (5) can be written

$$P_{n-1}(t) = \frac{\Gamma(n, \lambda t)}{\Gamma(n)} \tag{6}$$

which, on comparison with Eq. (10) of Section 1.6, shows the counting distribution to be Poisson.

1.11 Comment

The very brief outline of probability and statistics given in this chapter is no more than a statement of results with a few sketches of proofs. For a treatment of the discrete case, the reader is referred to the book of Feller [2], and for a good introduction to the continuous case, to the book of Munroe [3]. Feller's book has the additional advantage of containing (in its final chapters) excellent supplementary reading for Chapter 2.

By far the most important distribution in statistics is the normal distribution, which we have not mentioned. It appears that the normal distribution has not, so far, been very widely applied to road traffic theory, although there are many situations in which one would expect normality. This is undoubtedly a reflection of the immaturity of the theory; in a few years, normal distributions may be used in multivariate analysis of traffic data, as a model for Gaussian "noise" in the system or simply as the large sample approximation.

The Poisson distribution has been employed for many years to describe random processes in space (misprints, bomb bursts, insect counts) and in time (telephone calls, radioactive particles, deaths by horse kick). As we shall see in Chapter 4, there are several theoretical and practical objections to the uniform assumption that traffic is a Poisson process.

Unfortunately elementary textbooks on probability and statistics do not treat the mixed discrete and continuous case. In Section 1.5 we have given only a numerical example of this important type of distribution, but in Chapter 4 we will amplify and make use of the concept.

Similarly, the brief introduction to multivariate distributions will be enlarged in Chapter 7, where such distributions are used.

The student unfamiliar with transformations and generating functions may well wish for a more systematic classification of the auxiliary functions. The fact is that these transformations arose in different parts of applied mathematics for certain specific purposes, and that as a consequence, the information available, though vast, is not orderly. Consider, for example, the massive Bateman tables [7]. No discrete counterpart to these tables exists, although two of the transformations, Laplace (that is, moment generating function) and Mellin (that is, kth moment) have been used in both the discrete and continuous case by statisticians. Referring to Chapter 2 of Riordan's valuable book [4], the reader will find various other generating functions defined, and some relationships between them established. At present, however, the functions are used where they turn out to be useful; most often generating functions for the discrete case and Laplace transformations for the continuous.

In treating the distribution of sums of independent random variables, we touch on a very large and serious area of statistics. The statistical interest in this theory arises not from adding the distances between consecutive particles on an axis, but from sampling. If a sample of n items is drawn from a population $f(x)$, this is equivalent to supposing that random variables $x_1, \ldots, x_n$ are given, each of which has density $f(x)$. The mean, $(1/n) \sum x_i$, of the sample is essentially the sum of the n random variables, and many important statistical problems emerge from the natural desire to extract information regarding the population mean from the sample mean.

REFERENCES

1. Erdelyi, A., ed., "Tables of Integral Transforms" (Bateman Manuscript Project). California Inst. of Tech. McGraw-Hill, New York, 1954.
2. Feller, W., "Probability Theory and its Applications." Vol. 1. Wiley, New York, 1950.
3. Munroe, M. E., "Theory of Probability." McGraw-Hill, New York, 1951.
4. Riordan, J., "An Introduction to Combinatorial Analysis." Wiley, New York, 1958.

CHAPTER 2

Theory of Queues

2.1 Stochastic Processes

Suppose a random variable X with density $f(x)$ is a function of a real variable t; we think of $X(t)$ as the value of X at time t, and of $f(x; t)$ as the density at time t. All the other quantities associated with X will be functions of t: mean, $m(t)$; variance, $v(t)$; Laplace transform, $\pi(s; t)$; etc. Then $X(t)$ is called a *stochastic process* with cumulative distribution function

$$F(x; t) = \text{Prob}\,(X(t) \leqslant x)$$

in the continuous case and

$$P_n(t) = \text{Prob}\,(N(t) \leqslant n)$$

in the discrete case. It is important to notice that the functions associated with discrete stochastic processes are discrete in n and continuous in t, while those for continuous stochastic processes are continuous in both letters. One might also assume discrete time units, but we will have very little need for this.

If we imagine an ideal waiting line or queue, in which customers arrive at various points of time, and are served in turn by some facility, we can easily distinguish several stochastic processes associated with the system. In the present chapter, we will emphasize particularly three of these.

I. $N(t) =$ number of persons waiting at time t, including the one being served. It is always convenient to adopt the convention that the served person is included; otherwise there would be no distinction between an available service facility and one in which the single occupant was being served. Thus $N(t) = 0$ means that the facility is idle, $N(t) = 1$ means that the only occupant is being served, and in general

$p_n(t) =$ Prob ($n - 1$ are waiting and 1 is being served at time t), Domain: $0, 1, 2, \ldots$.

II. $X(t) =$ length of time that a person arriving at time t would have to wait before entering service. This is not necessarily the waiting time of any particular person, since there might be no entry to the system at time t. It is called the *virtual* waiting time, or if there is no confusion with the waiting time of a person, the waiting time. It is defined exclusive of the service time. Domain: $(0, \infty)$.

III. $N(t) =$ number of persons passing through the queue before it first becomes empty, beginning with r persons. Domain of definition: $r, r + 1, r + 2, \ldots$.

In this chapter, we investigate these processes in very simple circumstances, with a view to showing typical queue-theoretic methodology. Later, it will be possible to discuss the applicability of the results obtained to road traffic, and to adapt the methodology to several more complicated queueing problems which arise directly from road traffic.

2.2 Fundamental Definitions

The time between the arrival of the nth queuer and the $(n - 1)$st queuer is called the interarrival time of the nth queuer, and the length of time which the nth queuer will remain in service, his service time. Except for a few portions of Chapter 4, we will always assume the interarrival and service times to be *independent* random variables. If the interarrival and service distributions are given, together with the state of the system at time zero, all stochastic properties are completely specified.

In case arrivals occurred at random, and departures after service (with nonempty queue) also at random, the interarrival and service time distributions would be negative exponential. For a traffic light, it might be more realistic to assume that departures occurred during the green phase at equally spaced time intervals, so that the service time distribution would be deterministic. The two limiting situations (randomness and determinism) are the framework on which we will construct hypotheses more exactly suitable to road traffic.

Suppose the rate of arrival is λ and the rate of departure from a nonempty queue is μ; then the mean of the interarrival distribution is $1/\lambda$ and the mean of the service time distribution is $1/\mu$. The ratio of these quantities $\lambda/\mu = \rho$ is called the *traffic intensity* of the queue; the value of ρ relative to unity quite obviously tells whether the service facility is adequate to deal with the demand. In order to characterize the three cases $\rho < 1$, $\rho = 1$, and $\rho > 1$ more precisely, we introduce a few additional definitions.

When there are n customers in the system, the queue is said to be in state n, $n = 0, 1, 2, \ldots$. Thus $p_n(t)$ is the probability that the queue is in state n at time t.

Because of its intuitive simplicity,[†] we shall not prove the main theorem on simple queues:

I. If $\rho < 1$, every state is *recurrent*. That is, the probabilities $p_n(t)$ approach values p_n (as t approaches infinity) which satisfy $0 \leqslant p_n \leqslant 1$, $\Sigma p_n = 1$, and these *asymptotic state probabilities* are independent of the initial state of the system. This means that every possible queue length will occur a fixed proportion of time.

II. If $\rho > 1$, every state is *transient*. That is, each $p_n(t)$ approaches zero as t approaches infinity. The queue therefore becomes longer and longer, and the probability of any given state gradually dies out.

III. If $\rho = 1$, then the system is certain to return to any given state, but the average time between returns is infinite.

Except for a small digression in Chapter 6, we shall always be concerned with the first of these cases, in which the queue achieves equilibrium. If no equilibrium exists, or if the state probabilities

---

[†] And remoteness from the subject of this book.

are computed before the equilibrium is attained, each probability will be a time dependent function.

There is another circumstance in which the probabilities, even in equilibrium, will be time dependent, namely when the parameters λ and μ vary with time. The input process is said to be *homogeneous* if λ is independent of time. In many traffic problems it will be convenient to assume homogeneous demand over short periods, but it should be remembered that there exist well known traffic intensity patterns for days, weeks, and even years.

2.3 Random Arrivals and Departures

In Chapter 1, we have shown that random arrangements can be characterized in either one of two ways: (a) the counting distribution is Poisson, (b) the gap distribution is negative exponential. We now show that there is a third characterization of randomness. (c) Given a random arrangement with mean density λ and a small interval Δt, then

Prob (no points in Δt) $= 1 - \lambda \Delta t + o(\Delta t)$

Prob (one point in Δt) $= \lambda \Delta t + o(\Delta t)$ (1)

Prob ($>$ one point in Δt) $= o(\Delta t)$

where $o(\Delta t)^\dagger$ represents a quantity having the property

$$\lim_{\Delta t \to 0} \frac{o(\Delta t)}{\Delta t} = 0. \qquad (2)$$

In Section 1.6, Formula (11), we have shown that (a) implies (b), and in Section 1.10, Formula (6), that (b) implies (a). Now we prove that (c) implies, and is implied by (b).

Suppose the counting distribution is Poisson. Then

Prob (no points in Δt) $= e^{-\lambda \Delta t}$

$$= 1 - \lambda \Delta t + \tfrac{1}{2} (\lambda \Delta t)^2 - \ldots \qquad (1a)$$

$$= 1 - \lambda \Delta t + o(\Delta t)$$

---

† This is standard mathematical notation. In our use, it will invariably mean some function which contains the factor $(\Delta t)^2$. Note that $o(\Delta t) \pm o(\Delta t) = o(\Delta t)$.

Prob (one point in Δt) $= \lambda \Delta t \, e^{-\lambda \Delta t}$

$$= \lambda \Delta t \left(1 - \lambda \Delta t + \tfrac{1}{2} (\lambda \Delta t)^2 - \ldots\right)$$

$$= \lambda \Delta t + o(\Delta t) \qquad (1b)$$

Prob ($>$ one point in Δt) $= (1/n!) \, e^{-\lambda \Delta t} (\lambda \Delta t)^n, \qquad n > 1$

$$= o(\Delta t). \qquad (1c)$$

Suppose that Eq. (1) hold. Consider a time interval of length $t + \Delta t$, and divide it into the two subintervals $(0, t)$ and $(t, t + \Delta t)$, beginning at the origin for convenience. We require the probability $p_n(t)$ that there will be exactly n points in the first subinterval, and begin by calculating the probability $p_n(t + \Delta t)$ that there will be n points in the whole interval. For there to be n points in the whole interval, one of the following must hold:

0 in the first interval, n in the second

1 in the first interval, $n - 1$ in the second

2 in the first interval, $n - 2$ in the second

.

.

.

n in the first interval, 0 in the second.

The probabilities of these events are, respectively,

$$p_0(t) \, o(\Delta t)$$

$$p_1(t) \, (o\Delta t)$$

.

.

.

$$p_{n-1}(t) \, [\lambda \Delta t + o(\Delta t)]$$

$$p_n(t) \, [1 - \lambda \Delta t + o(\Delta t)].$$

Therefore

$$p_n(t + \Delta t) = \lambda \Delta t \, p_{n-1}(t) + (1 - \lambda \Delta t) \, p_n(t) + o(\Delta t)$$

which can be expressed in the form

$$\frac{p_n(t + \Delta t) - p_n(t)}{\Delta t} = \lambda \, p_{n-1}(t) - \lambda \, p_n(t) + \frac{o(\Delta t)}{\Delta t}. \tag{3}$$

Taking the limit as $\Delta t \to 0$, we have

$$p_n'(t) = \lambda \, p_{n-1}(t) - \lambda \, p_n(t) \qquad n = 1, 2, \ldots \tag{4}$$

where the prime denotes differentiation with respect to t. The argument above is valid only for $n > 0$, since otherwise the classification of possible location of points breaks down. It is not difficult to see that for the case $n = 0$, the resulting equation is

$$p_0'(t) = - \lambda \, p_0(t) \tag{5}$$

Equation (5) can be integrated at once, with the result

$$p_0(t) = e^{-\lambda t} \tag{6}$$

When this is substituted into the first equation of (4), we obtain

$$p_1'(t) = \lambda \, e^{-\lambda t} - \lambda \, p_1(t)$$

which is again a simple linear differential equation with solution

$$p_1(t) = \lambda \, t \, e^{-\lambda t}$$

Continuing in this way, or by applying more general methods to Eq. (4) we obtain the Poisson distribution. Hence, the three conditions are equivalent characterizations of randomness of points on a line.

In studying the simple queue, we first suppose randomness for arrivals and departures. It is customary (and more intuitive) to express this in terms of condition (c) for arrivals and condition (b) for service, as follows:

I. The probability of an arrival in a short time interval is proportional (proportionality constant $= \lambda$) to the length of the interval.

II. The service time is distributed negative exponentially, with mean $1/\mu$.

Let $p_n(t)$ denote the probability that the queue is in state n at time t, and consider the situation at time $t + \Delta t$. For the queue to be in state n at time $t + \Delta t$, exactly one of the following must hold at time t:

(a) It was in state n and no arrival or departure occurred. The probability of this is $p_n(t)(1 - \lambda\Delta t)(1 - \mu\Delta t) + o(\Delta t)$.

(b) It was in state $n - 1$, and an arrival occurred, but no departure. The probability of this is $p_{n-1}(t)\lambda\Delta t(1 - \mu\Delta t) + o(\Delta t)$.

(c) It was in state $n + 1$, and a departure occurred, but no arrival. The probability of this is $p_{n+1}(t)\mu\Delta t(1 - \lambda\Delta t) + o(\Delta t)$.

(d) Any other situation obtained. The probability of this is $o(\Delta t)$. Since $p_n(t + \Delta t)$ is the sum of these probabilities, we have

$$\frac{p_n(t + \Delta t) - p_n(t)}{\Delta t} = -(\lambda + \mu)\,p_n(t) + \lambda\,p_{n-1}(t) + \mu\,p_{n+1}(t) + \frac{o(\Delta t)}{\Delta t}.$$

$$(7)$$

When $n = 0$, this system of equations needs to be modified to read

$$\frac{p_0(t + \Delta t) - p_0(t)}{\Delta t} = -\lambda\,p_0(t) + \mu\,p_1(t) + \frac{o(\Delta t)}{\Delta t} \qquad (8)$$

as is easy to obtain by repeating the argument leading to Eq. (7). If we now pass to the limit as $\Delta t \to 0$, we obtain a set of differential difference equations in $p_n(t)$:

$$\frac{\partial}{\partial t}\,p_0(t) = -\lambda\,p_0(t) + \mu\,p_1(t) \qquad (9)$$

$$\frac{\partial}{\partial t}\,p_n(t) = -(\lambda + \mu)\,p_n(t) + \lambda\,p_{n-1}(t) + \mu\,p_{n+1}(t), \qquad n > 0.$$

Now we introduce the generating function

$$\pi(s, t) = \sum_{n=0}^{\infty} p_n(t)\,s^n \qquad 0 < s < 1,$$

multiply the nth equation of the set (9) by s^n, and add, obtaining

$$\frac{\partial}{\partial t}\,\pi(s, t) = \pi(s, t)\left[\mu\,\frac{1-s}{s} - \lambda(1-s)\right] - \mu\,\frac{1-s}{s}\,p_0(t). \qquad (10)$$

It is not difficult to solve this differential equation[†], but we are mainly interested in equilibrium, and therefore will make the simplifying assumption that the probabilities are not time dependent. The left side of (10) vanishes and the time argument is removed from the right side, giving

$$\pi(s) \, (\mu - \lambda s) - \mu \, p_0 = 0$$

or

$$\pi(s) = \frac{p_0}{1 - s\rho} \, . \tag{11}$$

Setting $s = 1$ in Eq. (11), we find that $p_0 = 1 - \rho$, and therefore

$$\pi(s) = \frac{1 - \rho}{1 - s\rho} \, . \tag{12}$$

It is only a matter of summing a geometric series to see that (11) is the generating function of the geometric distribution [Eq. (1) of Section 1.2]. Therefore

$$p_n = (1 - \rho) \, \rho^n \qquad n = 0, 1, 2, \ldots \tag{13}$$

are the asymptotic queue length probabilities. The mean and variance are given by Eq. (5) of Section 1.7. For a proper understanding of the behavior of queues, it is important to notice that the variance of the geometric distribution is always greater than its mean. When the queue approaches saturation, so that ρ is nearly unity, the variance becomes very large indeed. In practical terms this means that the average queue length, although possibly quite modest, is subject to enormous fluctuations which may lead to substantial waiting periods. For a more complete analysis of the question of delay, we now turn to an investigation of the virtual waiting time.

Consider the queue at time t, and let $w(x, t)$ be the density function of the waiting time distribution, so that

$$W(x, t) = \text{Prob (waiting time} \leqslant x \text{ at time } t)$$

[†] See Section 6.10, Reference *23a*.

is the cumulative distribution of waiting time. The queue is empty with probability $1 - \rho$, and in this case the waiting time is zero. Hence, $w(x, t)$ has a spike (or discrete component) at the origin, of height $1 - \rho$. In case the queue is not empty, the waiting time will be the sum of the service times of $n - 1$ persons waiting, plus the residual service time of the person in service. The distribution of service times is negative exponential, so the waiting time consists of the sum of $n - 1$ negative exponentially distributed variables, plus the residual waiting time of the person in service. It is a fourth characterization of randomness (which Feller asserts "puzzles unprepared minds") that the distribution of the length of a negative exponentially distributed variable remains the same if part of the length is chopped off. That is, after a time t_0 has been spent in service, the density of remaining time is still $\mu e^{-\mu x}$. This is a simple consequence of Bayes' Theorem. For, suppose

$$\text{Prob}\,(X \leqslant x) = 1 - e^{-\mu x}.$$

Then

$$\text{Prob}\,(X \leqslant x | X > x_0) = \frac{\text{Prob}\,(x_0 < X < x)}{\text{Prob}\,(X > x_0)}$$

$$= e^{\mu x_0} \int_{x_0}^{x} \mu\, e^{-\mu t}\, dt$$

$$= 1 - e^{-\mu(x - x_0)} \tag{14}$$

or with x_0 taken for the new time origin

$$= 1 - e^{-\mu x}.$$

Conversely, if $\text{Prob}\,(X \leqslant x | X > x_0) = \text{Prob}\,(X \leqslant x)$, then the events $X \leqslant x$ and $X > x_0$ are independent, and this was essentially the assumption upon which the derivation of the Poisson counting distribution was obtained.

Therefore, the waiting time is exactly the sum of n negative exponentially distributed variables, which we have shown to be distributed in the Type III form

$$\frac{\mu^n}{\Gamma(n)} e^{-\mu x} x^{n-1}. \tag{15}$$

But we have also shown that the probability of a queue of n members is exactly $(1-\rho)\rho^n$ in equilibrium, and therefore Eq. (15) represents the continuous component of $w(x|n)$, and $w(x)$ can be written

$$w(x) = (1-\rho)\,\delta(x) + \sum_{n=1}^{\infty} \frac{\mu^n e^{-\mu x} x^{n-1}}{\Gamma(n)} (1-\rho)\rho^n$$

$$= (1-\rho)\,\delta(x) + e^{-\mu x}(1-\rho)\lambda \sum_{n=0}^{\infty} \frac{(\lambda x)^n}{n!}$$

$$= (1-\rho)\,\delta(x) + \rho(\mu-\lambda)e^{-\mu x+\lambda x} \tag{16}$$

or, in cumulative form

$$W(x) = 1 - \rho\, e^{-\mu(1-\rho)x}. \tag{17}$$

There is a simple relationship between the generating function of the queue length distribution and the Laplace transform

$$\phi(s) = \int_0^{\infty} w(x) e^{-sx}\, dx$$

of the waiting time distribution which holds whenever service is negative exponential.

$$\phi(s) = \int_0^{\infty} \sum_{n=0}^{\infty} p_n \frac{\mu^n x^{n-1} e^{-\mu x}}{\Gamma(n)} e^{-sx}\, dx$$

$$= \sum_{n=0}^{\infty} p_n \frac{\mu^n}{\Gamma(n)} \int_0^{\infty} x^{n-1} e^{-(s+\mu)x}\, dx$$

$$= \sum_{n=0}^{\infty} p_n \frac{\mu^n}{(s+\mu)^n}$$

$$= \pi\left(\frac{\mu}{s+\mu}\right). \tag{18}$$

In the equilibrium case $\pi(s)$ is given by formula (12), and therefore the Laplace transform of (16) is

$$\phi(s) = \frac{(1-\rho)(s+\mu)}{s+\mu-\lambda} \tag{19}$$

which can be verified directly from Eq. (16). The mean and variance of the waiting time can be calculated from Eq. (19), keeping in mind that $m = -\phi'(0)$, $m_2 = \phi''(0)$, which follow from the definition of the Laplace transform. The results are

$$m = \frac{\rho}{\mu-\lambda} = \frac{1}{\mu}\frac{\rho}{1-\rho} \tag{20}$$

and

$$v = \frac{2\rho-\rho^2}{(\mu-\lambda)^2}. \tag{21}$$

Equation (16) is the first of several mixed discrete and negative exponential distributions which we shall encounter. It consists of the spike at the origin together with a negative exponential component beginning at the origin with parameter $(\mu-\lambda)$; this component is multiplied by ρ so that its area will be reduced from unity to ρ, because the height of the spike is $1-\rho$.

A general spike plus negative exponential distribution has four parameters, and can be written

$$(1-p)\,\delta(x-h) + p\beta\,e^{-(x-k)\beta},$$

where h is the location of the spike, k is the beginning of the negative exponential, β is the reciprocal mean of the continuous component, and p is the proportion allotted to the discrete component. In Chapters 4–7, we will have occasion to use several such distributions.

2.4 Random Arrivals

The methods and results of the preceding section are the simplest in queueing theory precisely because the "regenerative property of randomness," expressed in Eq. (14) applies to both arrivals and departures. This means that all instants of time are equivalent, in the sense that arrivals or departures are equally likely to occur. By way of contrast consider a constant service period of length $1/\mu$. The probability of a departure from a non-empty queue at a given instant is either zero or one. In situations intermediate between regularity and randomness, the probability of an occurrence increases with the lapse of time; the system is susceptible to an aging effect. Since the regenerative property was shown to be equivalent to the other definitions of randomness, any nonrandom process must exhibit aging.

Continuing the study of queue-theoretic methodology, we now give two typical arguments which can be used in case only one or the other process is random. For the purposes of traffic analysis, it will be more useful to retain the Poisson property for arrivals, and suppose the service mechanism to have an arbitrary cumulative distribution function

$$B(x) = \text{Prob (a service period} \leqslant x)$$

with density $b(x) = (d/dx)\, B(x)$ and Laplace transform

$$\beta(s) = \int_0^\infty e^{-sx}\, b(x)\, dx$$

The general principle is this: consider the queue only at moments when a departure takes place. At such times (called *points of regeneration*) the aging effect of nonrandom service is momentarily absent, since a new service period is just beginning.

Let the probability of n arrivals *during one service period* be k_n. Then k_n has the Poisson distribution with parameter λv, where v is a service period with density $b(x)$. Using an argument illustrated in Section 1.8 [leading to Eq. (5)], we find that

$$k_n = \int_0^\infty \frac{e^{-\lambda v}\, (\lambda v)^n}{n!}\, b(v)\, dv \tag{1}$$

with generating function

$$K(s) = \sum k_n s^n = \beta[\lambda(1-s)] \tag{2}$$

and mean value

$$K'(1) = \rho. \tag{3}$$

These quantities can be used to evaluate the probability of queue length changes between successive regeneration points. Let

p_{ij} = Prob (state j at a regeneration point | state i at preceding regeneration point).

Then, it is easy to see that

$$p_{0j} = k_j$$
$$p_{ij} = k_{j-i+1}, \qquad j-i+1 \geqslant 0, \qquad i > 0 \tag{4}$$
$$p_{ij} = 0 \quad \text{in all other cases.}$$

Moreover, the one stage transition probabilities p_{ij} must be related to the equilibrium probabilities p_i through the formulas

$$p_j = \sum_i p_{ij} p_i, \qquad j = 0, 1, 2, \ldots \tag{5}$$

since each state j must have been preceded by some state i and the appropriate transition from i to j. If the values (4) are substituted into Eq. (5), we find that the generating function

$$\pi(s) = \sum_j p_j s^j$$

can be written

$$\pi(s) = \sum_{j=0}^{\infty} \sum_{i=1}^{j+1} p_i k_{j-i+1} s^j + \sum_{j=0}^{\infty} p_0 k_j s^j$$

$$= \sum_{i=1}^{\infty} \sum_{j=i-1}^{\infty} p_i k_{j-i+1} s^j + p_0 K(s)$$

$$= \sum_{i=1}^{\infty} \sum_{l=0}^{\infty} p_i k_l s^{l+i-1} + p_0 K(s)$$

$$= \sum_{i=1}^{\infty} p_i s^{i-1} K(s) + p_0 K(s)$$

$$= (1/s) K(s) [\pi(s) - p_0] + p_0 K(s).$$

Solving for $\pi(s)$, we obtain

$$\pi(s) = \frac{p_0(1-s)\,K(s)}{K(s)-s}. \tag{6}$$

To evaluate p_0, we take the limit of $\pi(s)$ as $s \to 1$, making use of L'Hopital's rule.

$$1 = \mathrm{Lim}\,\pi(s) = \mathrm{Lim}\,\frac{p_0\,(1-s)\,K'(s) - p_0\,K(s)}{K'(s)-1}$$

$$= \frac{p_0}{1-\rho} \qquad \text{[from Eq. (3)]}$$

so that

$$\pi(s) = \frac{(1-\rho)(1-s)\,K(s)}{K(s)-s}. \tag{7}$$

Equations (2) and (7) taken together express the generating function for queue length in terms of the Laplace transform of the arbitrary service distribution. It is not difficult to deduce Eq. (12) of Section 2.3 from the fact that $\beta(s) = \mu/(s+\mu)$ for random departures.

The matrix $P = (p_{ij})$ is called the transition matrix for the system. It is an example of a stochastic matrix, in which all elements are non-negative and all row sums are unity. Many of the calculations relating to stochastic processes of this type can be expressed most compactly through the use of matrix notation. The fundamental property which permits such calculations is illustrated by the fact that P^2 is the matrix of transitions between semi-adjacent regeneration points. The elements of P^2 are

$$p_{ij}^{(2)} = \sum_l p_{il}\,p_{lj}$$

and this represents exactly the probability of a two step transition from state i to state j through any one of the possible intervening states l. Similarly P^n is the n-step transition matrix. Although we shall not make much use of matrix theoretic calculations in this book, it is occasionally convenient to exhibit the transition matrix as a brief definition of the process. For example, Eq. (4) could be written

$$P = \begin{pmatrix} k_0 & k_1 & k_2 & k_3 & \cdots \\ k_0 & k_1 & k_2 & k_3 & \cdots \\ 0 & k_0 & k_1 & k_2 & \cdots \\ 0 & 0 & k_0 & k_1 & \cdots \\ \vdots & \vdots & \vdots & \vdots & \end{pmatrix}.$$

Next, we consider the waiting time distribution, and obtain its Laplace transform by two different methods. The first of these is the use of a formula analogous to (18) of Section 2.3. That formula, it will be recalled, was valid for any simple queue with negative exponential *service*. In the present case we have negative exponential *interarrival* distribution. Consider a person leaving the queue after having spent a total time T waiting and being served, and suppose he leaves a queue of n behind him. Then

$$\pi(s) = \sum p_n s^n = \sum s^n \int_0^\infty \frac{1}{n!} e^{-\lambda T} (\lambda T)^n f(T) \, dT$$

where $f(T)$ is the density function for the distribution of T. Performing the summation, we find

$$\pi(s) = \int_0^\infty e^{-\lambda T + s\lambda T} f(T) \, dT$$

which is the Laplace transform of $f(T)$ with variable $\lambda(1 - s)$. However T is the sum of two variables, waiting time and service time, and therefore its Laplace transformation is the product of the separate Laplace transforms. Hence,

$$\pi(s) = \phi(\lambda (1 - s)) \beta(\lambda (1 - s)) \tag{8}$$

which is equivalent to

$$\phi(s) = \pi\left(\frac{\lambda - s}{\lambda}\right) \Big/ K(s) \tag{9}$$

$$= \frac{1 - \rho}{1 - (\lambda/s) [1 - \beta(s)]}$$

We shall next derive Eq. (9) by an argument relating directly to the waiting time distribution. If the virtual waiting time for a queue is represented as a function of time, it will decrease equally with time between arrival instants, and jump an amount equal to a service period at each arrival, as illustrated in Fig. 5. The instants where a jump takes place are random with parameter λ

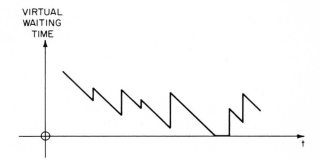

FIG. 5. Virtual waiting time.

and the heights of the jumps are random variables with density function $b(x)$. In time Δt the function has therefore decreased by an amount Δt [with probability $1 - \lambda \Delta t - o(\Delta t)$] or else increased an amount distributed as $b(x)$ [with probability $\lambda \Delta t + o(\Delta t)$]. If

$$W(x, t) = \text{Prob (waiting time} \leqslant x \text{ at time } t),$$

then we can write

$$W(x, t) = (1 - \lambda \Delta t + o(\Delta t)) \, W(x + \Delta t, t) +$$

$$(\lambda \Delta t + o(\Delta t)) \int_0^\infty B(x - y) \, w(y, t) \, dy + o(\Delta t),$$

where $w(x, t) = (\partial/\partial x) \, W(x, t)$. Transposing, dividing by Δt, and passing to the limit as $\Delta t \to 0$, we obtain

$$\frac{\partial W(x, t)}{\partial t} = \frac{\partial W(x, t)}{\partial x} - \lambda \, W(x, t) + \lambda \int_0^x B(x - y) \, w(x, t) \, dy. \quad (10)$$

If Eq. (10) is multiplied by e^{-sx} and integrated over x, it becomes

$$\frac{\partial \phi(s, t)}{\partial t} = w(s, t) \, [s - \lambda + \beta(s)] - s \, W(0, t), \tag{11}$$

keeping in mind that the Laplace transform of a convolution is the product of the Laplace transforms, and that the Laplace transform of a derivative is s times the Laplace transform minus the functional value at the origin.[†]

Assuming that equilibrium exists, the left side of Eq. (11) vanishes and the time argument is omitted in the right side, yielding

$$\phi(s) = \frac{w(0)}{1 - (\lambda/s) \, [1 - \beta(s)]}. \tag{12}$$

The probability of no waiting can be evaluated by the usual limiting argument, leading to $w(0) = 1 - \rho$, and Eq. (12) is seen to be identical with Eq. (9).

2.5 Random Arrivals; Regular Service

If every service period has length $1/\mu$,

$$b(x) = \delta(x - 1/\mu), \qquad \beta(s) = e^{-s/\mu} \tag{1}$$

and therefore,

$$\pi(s) = \frac{(1 - \rho)(1 - s)}{1 - s \, e^{-\rho(s-1)}}. \tag{2}$$

The denominator of this fraction is the sum of a geometric series, and hence the generating function can be written

$$\pi(s) = (1 - \rho)(1 - s) \sum_{i=0}^{\infty} (s \, e^{\rho} \, e^{-\rho s})^{i} \tag{3}$$

---

† This can be proven easily by integration by parts.

for s satisfying $s\,e^\rho < e^{s\rho}$. The term of (3) independent of s is

$$p_0 = 1 - \rho, \tag{4}$$

and the coefficient of s is

$$p_1 = (1 - \rho)(e^\rho - 1). \tag{5}$$

Therefore

$$\pi(s) - p_0 - sp_1 = \sum_{i=2}^{\infty} \sum_{j=0}^{\infty} e^{i\rho}\, s^i\, \frac{(-s\rho i)^j}{j!}, \tag{6}$$

and the coefficient of s^n is

$$p_n = (1 - \rho) \sum_{i+j=n} \frac{(-\rho i)^j e^{\rho i}}{j!} - (1 - \rho) \sum_{i+j=n-1} \frac{(-\rho i)^j e^{\rho i}}{j!}$$

$$= (1 - \rho) \left[\sum_{i=0}^{n} \frac{(-\rho i)^{n-i} e^{\rho i}}{(n-i)!} - \sum_{i=0}^{n-1} \frac{(-\rho i)^{n-i-1} e^{\rho i}}{(n-i-1)!} \right]. \tag{7}$$

Equations (4), (5), and (7) give the asymptotic queue length probabilities for the case of random arrivals and regular service. The moments of this distribution can be obtained from the values of

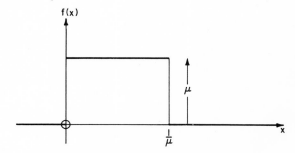

FIG. 6. The rectangular distribution.

p_n or by noting that the moment generating function is $\pi(e^s)$, but either procedure leads to heavy calculations and will be omitted.

The waiting time distribution for regular service can be found quite easily from general principles. Since arrivals are at random, each arrival is equally likely to arrive at any point of a service interval, if the queue is not empty. This means that the residual service at the moment of arrival is distributed uniformly on the interval $(0, 1/\mu)$. Such a distribution is called rectangular for an obvious reason, and is illustrated in Fig. 6. When an arrival finds $n - 1$ persons waiting and one in service, the waiting time cannot be less than $(n - 1)/\mu$ nor more than n/μ, and is equally likely to have any value in between. Furthermore, the probability of a wait between $(n - 1)/\mu$ and n/μ is precisely the value p_n given

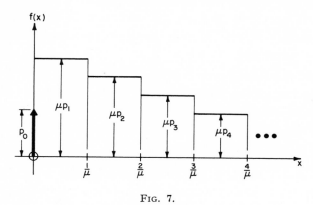

FIG. 7.

by Eq. (4), (5), and (7). Hence the waiting time distribution consists of continuous blocks of height μp_n over the intervals $[(n - 1)/\mu, n/\mu]$ together with a discrete spike at the origin of height p_0. This distribution, illustrated in Fig. 7, is the one having Laplace transform

$$\frac{s(1 - \rho)}{s - \lambda + \lambda e^{-s/\mu}}$$

by virtue of Eq. (8) of Section 2.4.

2.6 Busy Period

Next we consider the third of the stochastic processes connected with queues which was proposed in Section 2.1, namely the probability $p_n(r, \rho)$ that in a queue with traffic intensity ρ in state r, exactly n persons will pass through the system before it first becomes empty.

In order for the queue to vanish for the first time when exactly n persons have passed through it, two conditions must be met:

(a) there must be exactly $n - r$ arrivals in the n service periods, and

(b) these arrivals must fall into the individual service periods in such a way that (i) the queue never becomes empty before the nth service period is finished, and (ii) there is no arrival during the last service period. Arrival patterns satisfying (i) and (ii) will be called admissible.

The proportions of admissible and inadmissible arrival patterns is independent of the distribution of service periods, as well as of condition (a). The probability of condition (a) is a simple generalization of formula (1) of Section 2.4, and can be written

$$R_{n-r,n} = \int_0^\infty \frac{(\lambda v)^{n-r} e^{-\lambda v}}{(n-r)!} b^{n*}(v)\, dv, \tag{1}$$

which becomes

$$\binom{2n-r-1}{n-r} \frac{\rho^{n-r}}{(1+\rho)^{2n-r}} \tag{2}$$

for negative exponential service and

$$\frac{e^{-n\rho}(n\rho)^{n-r}}{(n-r)!} \tag{3}$$

for regular service. To evaluate the probability of (b), we choose Eq. (2), and assume $\rho < 1$, so that the busy period will end with probability one. We then wish to find constants $A_{n,r}$ having the property that

$$\sum_{n=r}^\infty A_{n,r}\binom{2n-r-1}{n-r} \frac{\rho^{n-r}}{(1+\rho)^{2n-r}} = 1, \tag{4}$$

or, equivalently, constants $B_{n,r}$ such that

$$\sum_{n=r}^{\infty} B_{n,r} \frac{\rho^{n-r}}{(1+\rho)^{2n-r}} = 1. \tag{5}$$

Let

$$\beta = \frac{\rho}{(1+\rho)^2}, \qquad d\beta = \frac{1-\rho}{(1+\rho)^3}, \tag{6}$$

and define

$$f(\beta) = \sum_{n=r}^{\infty} B_{n,r}\, \beta^n = \left(\frac{\rho}{1+\rho}\right) \tag{7}$$

Since this is a Maclaurin series for $f(\beta)$, we must have

$$B_{n,r} = \frac{1}{n!} \frac{d^n}{d\beta^n} f(\beta)\big|_{\beta=0} \tag{8}$$

$$= \frac{1}{2\pi i} \int_C \frac{f(\beta)}{\beta^{n+1}}\, d\beta, \tag{9}$$

where C is a closed contour in the complex plane surrounding the multiple pole at the origin. Substituting from (6) and (7),

$$B_{n,r} = \frac{1}{2\pi i} \int_C \left(\frac{\rho}{1+\rho}\right)^r \frac{(1+\rho)^{2n+2}}{\rho^{n+1}} \frac{1-\rho}{(1+\rho)^3}\, d\rho \tag{10}$$

$$= \frac{1}{2\pi i} \int_C \frac{(1+\rho)^{2n-r-1}}{\rho^{n-r+1}}\, d\rho - \frac{1}{2\pi i} \int_C \frac{(1+\rho)^{2n-r-1}}{\rho^{n-r}}\, d\rho$$

$$= \frac{1}{(n-r)!} \frac{d^{n-r}}{d\rho^{n-r}} (1+\rho)^{2n-r-1}\big|_{\rho=0} -$$

$$\frac{1}{(n-r-1)!} \frac{d^{n-r-1}}{d\rho^{n-r-1}} (1+\rho)^{2n-r-1}\big|_{\rho=0}$$

$$= \frac{(2n-r-1)!}{(n-r)!\,(n-1)!} - \frac{(2n-r-1)!}{(n-r-1)!\,n!}$$

$$= \frac{r}{n} \binom{2n-r-1}{n-1} \tag{11}$$

so that

$$A_{n,r} = \frac{r}{n},$$

a result valid for any distribution of service times. Consequently, for $\rho < 1$, the probability that n will pass through a queue of traffic intensity ρ, beginning with r in the queue is

$$p_n = \frac{r}{n}\binom{2n-r-1}{n-r}\frac{\rho^{n-r}}{(1+\rho)^{2n-r}}, \qquad n = r, r+1, r+2, \ldots$$

$$(12)$$

for negative exponential service, and

$$p_n = \frac{r}{n}\frac{e^{-n\rho}(n\rho)^{n-r}}{(n-r)!}, \qquad n = r, r+1, r+2, \ldots \qquad (13)$$

for regular service.

Now let us re-examine formulas (12) and (13) without the restriction $\rho < 1$. Although the value $A_{n,r} = r/n$ was obtained by the device of assuming $\rho < 1$ so that $\Sigma p_n = 1$, the result is a purely combinatorial one, and quite independent of the behavior of the queue, or indeed of there being any queue in question. Condition (a), although dependent upon the queueing problem for its meaning, is also perfectly true for $\rho \geqslant 1$. However, the probability distributions (12) and (13) will not (as we prove in a moment) add up to one when $\rho > 1$. The remaining element of probability $1 - \Sigma p_n$ represents the probability that the queue will never again be empty, and is denoted by p_∞. As ρ increases, it is natural to expect $p_\infty \to 1$.

Suppose $\rho \geqslant 1$; we shall consider first the case of regular service, and write

$$\sum_{n=r}^{\infty} p_n = \sum_{n=r}^{\infty} C_{n,r}\,\beta^{n-r}\,e^{-\rho r}, \qquad (14)$$

where

$$C_{n,r} = \frac{r}{(n-r)!}\,n^{n-r-1} \qquad (15)$$

and

$$\beta = \rho\, e^{-\rho}.\tag{16}$$

Equation (16) defines a function with a unique maximum $(\beta = 1/e)$ at the point $\rho = 1$, as shown in Fig. 8. Let ρ' denote the smaller

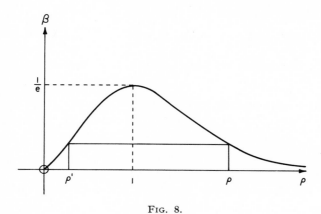

FIG. 8.

value of ρ which yields the same β. Then Eq. (14) can be written

$$1 - p_\infty = \sum_{n=r}^{\infty} C_{n,r}\, \beta_{n-r}\, e^{-\rho r}$$

$$= e^{(\rho' - \rho)r},$$

or, using Eq. (16),

$$p_\infty = 1 - (\rho'/\rho)^r.\tag{17}$$

In the intermediate case $\rho = 1$, we have $\rho = \rho'$, and therefore $p_\infty = 0$. The value ρ' can be found if the function $\beta = \rho\, e^{-\rho}$ is expressed in the form $\rho = \rho(\beta)$ by means of Lagrange series, and is

$$\rho' = \sum_{i=1}^{\infty} \frac{i^{i-1}}{i!}\, \beta^i,\tag{18}$$

where β is computed from Eq. (16).

As in the other two problems, the results for Poisson service are considerably simpler. The function analogous to Eq. (16) is

$$\beta = \frac{\rho}{(1+\rho)^2},$$

(19)

which leads again to a maximum at $\rho = 1$. In this case, however,

$$\rho \rho' = 1,$$

(20)

a formula obtainable by easy algebra, and hence the equations

$$1 - p_\infty = \left(\frac{1+\rho}{\rho}\right)^r \sum_n B_{n,r} \beta^n$$

and

$$1 = \left(\frac{1+\rho'}{\rho'}\right)^r \sum_n B_{n,r} \beta^n$$

yield

$$p_\infty = (1/\rho)^r.$$

(21)

2.7 Mean Values

In the preceding sections, we have investigated three different stochastic processes associated with the simple queue under a variety of circumstances, all of which have in common a random arrival pattern. Differentiation of Eq. (8), Section 2.4, which is valid for all random input, gives, upon setting $s = 1$,

$$\bar{u} = \lambda \bar{v} + \lambda \bar{w} = \lambda W,$$

(1)

where

$\bar{u} =$ mean queue length

$\bar{v} =$ mean service time $(= 1/\mu$ in this section)

$\bar{w} =$ mean waiting time

$W =$ mean total time in the system $= \bar{w} + \bar{v}$.

If the service time distribution is known, Eq. (1) enables the various means to be expressed in terms of each other. There is a trick for obtaining one of these to begin with. Let n and n' denote the queue lengths at two successive regeneration points, assuming equilibrium. Then n and n' share the same probability distribution and therefore the same moments. Also

$$n' = \max (n - 1, 0) + k, \tag{2}$$

where k is the number of arrivals between regeneration points, with distribution given by Eq. (1) of Section 2.4. Equation (2) can be written

$$n' = n + k + \delta(n) - 1. \tag{3}$$

Squaring Eq. (3), we obtain {since $[\delta(n)]^2 = \delta(n)$}

$$n'^2 = n^2 - 2n(1 - k) + (k - 1)^2 + \delta(n) (2k - 1), \tag{4}$$

and using the expectation operator (cf. Section 1.7),

$$0 = - 2 E(n)(1 - E(k)) +$$

$$E(k^2) - 2 E(k) + 1 + E[\delta(n)][E(2k) - 1].$$

Since $E[\delta(n)] = 1 - \rho$, which follows by taking the expectation of Eq. (3), we have

$$E(n) = \rho + \frac{E[k(k - 1)]}{2(1 - \rho)}$$

or

$$\bar{u} = \rho + \frac{\lambda^2 \text{ var } (v) + \rho^2}{2(1 - \rho)}, \tag{5}$$

where var (v) is the variance of the service time distribution. Equations (1) and (5) are particularly easy to use, since var $(v) = 0$ for regular service and var $(v) = 1/\mu^2$ for negative exponential service. The values in the following table can be deduced from Equations (1) and (5), and confirmed by integration or summation of the appropriate probability distribution, as given in Sections 2.3 and 2.5.

	Mean queue length	Mean waiting time	Mean waiting plus service time
Random service	$\dfrac{\rho}{1-\rho}$	$\dfrac{1}{\mu}\dfrac{\rho}{1-\rho}$	$\dfrac{1}{\lambda}\dfrac{\rho}{1-\rho}$
Regular service	$\dfrac{2\rho-\rho^2}{2(1-\rho)}$	$\dfrac{\rho}{2\mu(1-\rho)}$	$\dfrac{2-\rho}{2\mu(1-\rho)}$

Any comparison of the two rows above will reveal the advantage of regular service periods over negative exponentially distributed service periods. It is interesting, however, that this does not show up in the third stochastic process which we have considered, the busy period. In fact, some calculations will show that both the distributions (12) and (13) of Section 2.6 have the same mean value, namely

$$\frac{r}{1-\rho}. \tag{6}$$

2.8 Generalizations

An interesting property of the Type III distribution with parameters k, μ, is that it forms a natural bridge between randomness and regularity. We have already noted that for $k = 1$, the Type III density becomes negative exponential. Furthermore, since its mean is k/μ and its variance k/μ^2, if we let both k and μ approach infinity in such a way that the mean is held constant, the variance approaches zero, giving a deterministic distribution at the mean. Such a distribution corresponds to regular spacing. A process with Type III gaps between events is called an *Erlang process* of order k. Since a Type III distribution can also be interpreted as the distribution of the sum of k negative exponential gaps, the Erlang process can be obtained by taking every kth point of a random process. This fact is used in queueing theory by interpreting Erlang service as a mechanism having k

negative exponential stages. The principal application which we will make rests on the more general property of being intermediate between randomness and regularity. It should not be supposed that the Erlang process is the only one which can serve this purpose; it is, however, one which is well known in statistical theory and expressible as a simple function.

There is very little difficulty in modifying the equations of Section 2.4 since the Laplace transform of the Type III service distribution is

$$\phi(s) = \left(\frac{\mu}{\mu + s}\right)^k. \tag{1}$$

In Section 2.6, it is only necessary to note that the n-fold convolution of a Type III distribution with parameters μ and k is another Type III distribution with parameters μ and nk, which should be clear from Eq. (1), keeping in mind that the Laplace transform of the n-fold convolution is ϕ^n. Placing this value in Eq. (1) of Section 2.6 gives very quickly a generalization of formulas (12) and (13) of that section. In Chapter 4, we shall return to the Erlang process in a specifically traffic context.

If we let the number of servers be n, then any simple queue can be characterized by three symbols, indicating respectively input process, service process, and number of servers.

With the notation

$$D = \text{deterministic}$$
$$M = \text{random}$$
$$E_k = \text{Erlang of order } k$$
$$G = \text{arbitrary,}$$

we have been considering in Section 2.3 the queueing system $M/M/1$, in Section 2.4 the queueing system $M/G/1$, and in Section 2.5 the queueing system $M/D/1$.

However, this classification takes into account the characteristics of only one particular type of queue. There are many other complications in queueing theory of which we will have occasion to use the following:

(a) A congestion system with *loss* rather than *waiting*. If a channel is occupied, the arrival goes away, as in one classical case of an n place telephone switchboard. Parking lots also form an excellent example of a queueing system with loss.

(b) Between loss systems and waiting systems are queues with *balking*. Each arrival may join the queue or go away, depending on how long the queue is, and on his individual tastes. Such a system might be used at a busy intersection, if each driver has the option of taking some alternative route.

(c) Queues in disequilibrium will be treated briefly in connection with the rush hour.

(d) A *bulk service* mechanism takes items into service in batches, rather than individually. Certain properties of traffic lights are best treated as bulk service during green phases.

(e) Traffic abounds with situations in which the service process is very complicated indeed. The study of these *delay problems* often reduces to a question of finding the service distribution from the actual mechanics and statistics of the delay in question. Different results are obtained for a stop sign, for merging into a freeway, and for passing on an open road.

(f) The gaps between successive arrivals or departures may not be independent. There are good reasons (both theoretical and experimental) to suppose that the gap preceding a car and the gap following a car are each influenced by the behavior of the car and are therefore not in general independent.

2.9 Comment

The history of queueing theory falls neatly into two periods, separated by the very important paper of D. G. Kendall [15]. In the first period, beginning with the work of Erlang [4] early in this century and lasting until 1951, the principal investigators were continental Europeans, who were concerned with problems of telephone traffic. Their publications were often recondite, appeared in relatively inaccessible journals, and frequently in obscure languages.

Within the past ten years, the situation has been almost reversed. The theory is being applied to a multitude of phenomena; its results appear mainly in the English language. At present, road traffic investigations are only beginning to make use of these results, for the formulation in vehicular terms (as we shall see in succeeding chapters) is rather difficult. The intrinsic properties of vehicles which contrast most strongly with telephone calls will be systematically investigated in Chapter 3.

Nearly all of the material in the present chapter can be found in Kendall's papers [15, 16], and the reader wishing a more exact and logical treatment of the subject should read these papers after Feller's Chapters 15–17 [7]. Another compact introduction to queueing methodology for the simple waiting and loss systems is given by Khintchine [17].

There are several good collections of queueing formulas, which will furnish the reader with an idea of the range of complication and application of the subject: Fry [8], which is based mainly on Erlang's work, Saaty [21], Haller et al. [14], and Morse [19], as well as two bibliographies, Riley [20] and Doig [6]. On the more general subject of stochastic processes, the books of Takács [23] and Bharucha-Reid [2] are recommended.

Although it will appear later that the Poisson distribution has serious defects in car counting, it continues to form a point of departure for generalizations. Hadley and Whitin [10] summarize a large number of properties of this distribution.

The system of differential-difference equations leading to Eq. (10) of Section 2.3 are called the Kolmogorov equations for the simple queue; we shall use this technique in a number of other special situations. Section 2.4 is taken largely from Kendall's paper [15], with the exception of the waiting time derivation in Eq. (10)–(12), which is treated in more generality and with greater rigor by Takacs [22]. The regular service case of Section 2.5 is due originally to Erlang [4], and is given by Fry [8] and quoted by Saaty [21]. A general treatment of stochastic matrix theory will be found in Chapters 14 and 15 of Bellman [1]. A direct contrast between various service distributions is given by Gaver [9].

Formula (13) of Section 2.6 is called the Borel-Tanner distribution, or in case $r = 1$, Borel's distribution. It was discovered by
Borel [3], using an argument similar to that leading to Eq. (11),
and generalized by Tanner [24]. It has also been studied by
Haight and Breuer [13] and recently proved by combinatorial
methods by Tanner [25]. Equation (18) can be obtained directly
from (16) by using the Bromwich [5] section on Lagrange series.
Equation (12) has been studied by Haight [11, 12]. For a parallel
line of development (via the „Ballot Problem") see Takács [23a]

In Section 2.7, Eq. (1) holds very generally, as proved by
Little [18]. Equation (5) is called the Pollaczek-Khintchine
formula, and is proved (the method we use here) by Kendall [15].
In Section 4.2 we will give more agreeable proof.

The classification system used in Section 2.8 is also due to
Kendall [16]. It is important to note that a different name is
given to the *process* (or arrangement) and to the *distributions*
which characterize it. We have systematically used "random
process," "Poisson counting distribution" and "negative exponential gap distribution". For E_k, we shall say "Erlang process" and
"Type III gap distribution." Many authors call the random
process a Poisson process and the Type III distribution an Erlang
distribution. However, in view of the importance of this distinction
in Chapter 4, and of a further dichotomy which will be established
there, it is necessary to enforce a rigid separation of ideas in the
beginning. The four characterizations of random points on a line
are thus: (a) Poisson counting, (b) negative exponential gaps,
(c) Eq. (1) of Section 2.3, and (d) absence of aging. In Chapter 4
and elsewhere we shall generalize (b) and look for expressions
analogous to (a), (c), and (d) as needed.

REFERENCES

1. Bellman, R. E., "Introduction to Matrix Analysis." McGraw-Hill, New York,
   1960.
2. Bharucha-Reid, A. T., "Elements of the Theory of Markov Processes and Their
   Applications." McGraw-Hill, New York, 1960.
3. Borel, E., Sur l'emploi du Théorème de Bernoulli pour Faciliter le Calcul d'un

Infinité de Coefficients. Application au Problème de L'attente à un Guichet. *Compt. rend. acad. sci. Paris* **214**, 452–456 (1942).

4. Brockmeyer, E., Halstrøm, H. L., and Jensen, A., "The Life and Works of A. K. Erlang." Copenhagen Telephone Co., Copenhagen, 1948.

5. Bromwich, T. J. I'a., "An Introduction to the Theory of Infinite Series." Macmillan, London, 1955.

6. Doig, A., A Bibliography on the Theory of Queues. *Biometrika* **44**, Parts 3 and 4, 490–514 (1957).

7. Feller, W., "Probability Theory and its Applications," Vol. 1 Wiley, New York, 1950.

8. Fry, T. C., "Probability and its Engineering Uses." Van Nostrand, New York, 1928.

9. Gaver, D. P., The Influence of Servicing Times in Queueing Processes. *J. Operations Research Soc. Am.* **2**, No. 2, 139–149 (1954).

10. Hadley, G., and Whitin, T. M., Useful Properties of the Poisson Distribution. Letter to Editor. *Operations Research* **9**, No. 3, 408–10 (May-June 1961).

11. Haight, F. A., A Distribution Analogous to the Borel-Tanner. *Biometrika* **48**, 167–73 (1961).

12. Haight, F. A., Expected Utility for Queues Servicing Messages with Exponentially Decaying Utility. *Ann. Math. Statist.* **32**, No. 2, 587–93 (June 1961).

13. Haight, F. A., and Breuer, M. A., The Borel-Tanner Distribution. *Biometrika* **47**, 143–50 (1960).

14. Haller, Raymond and Brown, Inc., "Queueing Theory Applied to Military Communications Systems." Armed Services Technical Information Agency Manual AD 88217 (Feb. 1, 1956).

15. Kendall, D. G., Some Problems in the Theory of Queues. *J. Roy. Statist. Soc.,* Ser. B, **13**, No. 2, 151–85 (1951).

16. Kendall, D. G., Stochastic Processes Occurring in the Theory of Queues and their Analysis by the Method of the Imbedded Markov Chain. *Ann. Math. Statist.* **24**, No. 3, 338–54 (Sept. 1953).

17. Khintchine, A. Y., "Mathematical Methods in the Theory of Queueing." No. 7 of Griffin's Statistical Monographs and Courses. Griffin, London, 1960.

18. Little, J. D. C., A Proof for the Queuing Formula: $L = \lambda W$. *Operations Research* **9**, No. 3, 383–87 (May-June 1961).

19. Morse, P. M., "Queues, Inventories and Maintenance." Wiley, New York, 1958.

20. Riley, V., Bibliography of Queueing Theory. *In* "Operations Research for Management," Vol. II, pp. 541–56. Johns Hopkins Press, Baltimore, Maryland, 1956.

21. Saaty, T. L., Resume of Useful Formulas in Queueing Theory. *Operations Research* **5**, 161–200 (1957).

22. Takács, L., Investigation of Waiting Time Problems by Reduction to Markov Processes. *Acta Math. Acad. Sci. Hungary* **6**, 101–29 (1955)

23. Takács, L., "Stochastic Processes." Wiley, New York, 1960.

23a. Takács, L., A Generalization of the Ballot Problem and its Application in the Theory of Queues. *J. Am. Statist. Assoc.* **57**, No. 298, 327–37 (June, 1962).

24. Tanner, J. C., A Problem of Interference Between Two Queues. *Biometrika* **40**, 58–69 (1953).

25. Tanner, J. C., A Derivation of the Borel Distribution. *Biometrika* **48**, 222–24 (June 1961).

CHAPTER **3**

Fundamental Characteristics
of Road Traffic

3.1 Introduction

Road traffic theory is concerned with the movement of discrete objects[†] over a two-dimensional network. It shares this much with several other theories, for example, telephone traffic theory and inventory theory. In this section, three fundamental properties of road traffic will be given, which characterize it as a separate system.

A. AMBIGUITY. The control over these objects rests in part with individual drivers and in part with a unified system. The objects do not move as freely as Brownian particles or with the constraint of scheduled items such as railroad cars. They are subject to certain controls, of which the avoidance of collision is basic, but cannot be considered a proper subject for complete regulation. In supplying the network with control devices such as stop signs, traffic lights and one way streets, the traffic engineer must always realize that individual drivers will retain some control over their vehicles and will use their control to achieve their own purposes and may evade or even disobey the rules. In mathematical terms, this means that equilibrium conditions are essentially built in to the system, and are a matter for observation and description rather that invention. There are of course, local variations from

---

[†] Which we will call cars or vehicles, unless there is some particular need to distinguish different categories of vehicles.

equilibrium, such as the traffic jam; but these are (so far) self-dissipating.

Ambiguity has also a deeper aspect, especially meaningful in city planning and land use for transportation. The desires of individual drivers can be only partially sacrificed to social efficiency; any scheme proposed must take into account the ambiguous role of private transportation. It is an unrealistic solution to a traffic problem which schedules drivers by forcing them to adopt incorrect origins or destinations or intolerable delays.

In this respect the problems of road traffic are quite different from network problems previously studied by mathematical methods. The question of optimal design hardly arises (except for small local parts of the system) and optimal scheduling is meaningless. In addition, the number of vehicles and the number of intersections far exceeds those found in classical network studies.

B. FINITENESS. The physical dimensions of the vehicles and of the network are compatible quantities, so that the possibility of local interference and congestion exists. Congestion arises not entirely from some servicing delay (as in the theory of queueing) but possibly from the mere interaction of the cars on roads. The speed with which the cars travel is also finite (in contrast to telephone messages), and will vary from car to car and from time to time. Speeds are generally depressed by additional quantity of vehicles, which is roughly the reverse of the fluid situation, where velocity is increased by constraint.

Models which ignore this postulate and treat vehicular traffic flow like telephone traffic cannot be considered sufficiently realistic to be recognizable as road models. For example, a sequence of traffic lights on a single road would be relatively easy to analyze as a series of queues. When the finite speed and finite car length are introduced the question is very much complicated. If the wishes of individual drivers are also taken into account, and a probability of leaving the system by right or left turning is postulated, still more difficulty arises. Finally, the left turning maneuver might be considered in detail, with its consequent interruption of, or control by, the oncoming lanes of traffic.

C. TIME-SPACE. Considered as a stochastic process, the position of cars in space and in time are not identical. This is a simple consequence of the variability in speeds, and contrasts sharply with processes involving radioactive particles, telephone calls, and other recurrent events. In all the latter cases, the two dimensions of time and space, if distinguishable at all, are congruent. Such is not even approximately true for road traffic. Variations in speed are by no means negligible; in fact it is precisely speed variations (and route variations) which offer the driver the opportunity to control effectively his contribution to the traffic scene.

The time-space dichotomy will arise in virtually every part of road traffic theory. If it is momentarily neglected, this will be only to reintroduce the question at a more sophisticated level. Relationships between cars in space and cars in time have a particularly important role to play in empirical studies, for the time measurements (by means of road tapes, photoelectric cells, etc.) are characteristically easy for the traffic engineer to perform, whereas space measurements require, at present, extremely accurate and far reaching aerial photography. Even if such systems of photography were possible, instantaneous values of speed and acceleration could not be obtained, except by approximating from several consecutive views.

These three characteristics might perhaps be augmented with various others, but in a general way they divide road problems from nearby mathematical areas which the reader might initially regard as identical. In the chapters which follow, a recurring theme will be modification or adaptation of results because of the fundamental requirements.

3.2 The Fundamental Diagram of Road Traffic

Everyone knows that

$$(distance) = (speed)(time) \tag{1}$$

but the meaning of this formula for a collection of vehicles needs to be carefully considered. In the first place, it is customary to write it in the reciprocal form

(cars per time) = (distance per time)(cars per distance)

or in symbols

$$\rho = \lambda\, u \tag{2}$$

where

ρ = flow = volume† (cars/time)

λ = concentration = density† (cars/distance)

u = speed

There are several possible variations in these quantities suggested in the preceding section, and it is clear that formula (2) has an alternate form in which the speed u is replaced, for a collection of cars, by the mean speed m:

$$\rho = m\, \lambda \tag{3}$$

where λ and ρ are still assumed constant. This too is not clear, since there are many different distributions which might be used to compute m, λ, and ρ. They will be defined more exactly in Chapter 4, but for the moment it will be sufficient to consider the following possibilities:

I. Referring to a single car.
    1. Its speed distribution for points in space (distance/time).
    2. Its speed distribution for points in time (distance/time).
    3. Its gap distribution to the next car in space, called *spacing* (distance).
    4. Its gap distribution to the next car in time, called *headway* (time).

---

† In literature of traffic theory, the unsuitable symbols q = flow, k = concentration, are frequently used. Note that although λ and ρ as defined here, are not the queue-theoretic λ and ρ, either one may correspond to λ or μ of Chapter 2, depending on whether the context involves space or time.

II. Referring to all cars at a fixed point in space or time.
   1. The speed distribution for fixed time (distance/time).
   2. The speed distribution for fixed space (distance/time).
   3. The headway distribution at a fixed place (time).
   4. The spacing distribution at a fixed time (distance).

III. Distributions computed for all cars over all points in time or space.

Taking into consideration the variety of distributions possible, it is obvious that Formula (3) can have a number of different interpretations in different circumstances. In each case ρ relates to *reciprocal mean headway* and λ to *reciprocal mean spacing*.

However, the difficulty with Formula (3) does not stop here. It is also true from the general principles of Section 3.1 that both λ and ρ depend on velocity. Since increased density of vehicles leads to decreased speeds, the correct *functional* form for (3) is

$$\rho(\lambda) = \lambda\, m(\lambda) \qquad (4)$$

Therefore, the significance of Formula (1) is simply that it is only necessary to find either function $\rho(\lambda)$ or $m(\lambda)$; then (4) gives the other. At this point, it is useful to remember some basic limiting properties of road traffic, as directly experienced.

Of the three quantities λ, ρ, u, only λ has a theoretical maximum value, which corresponds to solidly packed cars, and which we will denote by λ'. This can be imagined to be the reciprocal of a car length, say $(15 \text{ ft})^{-1}$. It may also be true that m and ρ have some observed maximum, but it is not practical to assign any absolute upper limit to flow or speed. This is quite analogous to our arguments in Chapter 1 regarding the "correct" domain of definition for random variables. We would prefer to assume that the right tail of the distribution of speeds is asymptotic to the axis rather than truncated at any particular point.

In this interpretation, u is a random variable, and consequently (2) is a relationship between random variables. If the average is taken in one of the senses mentioned above, (4) would be a relationship between real functions of λ and consequently in a particular situation there might be an observable maximum value of ρ, regarded as a function of λ. This quantity, which we will consider in detail later, is of great interest to traffic engineers and is called by them the *capacity* of the road.

Jampacked traffic is stationary; therefore the flow is zero, $\rho(\lambda') = 0$. If there are no cars, flow is also zero, $\rho(0) = 0$. Between these two obvious extremes lies an unknown function, $\rho = \rho(\lambda)$, as illustrated in Fig. 9. This flow-concentration diagram we call the *Fundamental Diagram of Road Traffic*.

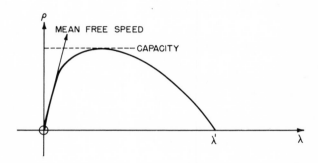

FIG. 9. The fundamental diagram of road traffic.

Many of the properties of road traffic as set forth in Section 3.1 are reflected in the Fundamental Diagram: the time-space relationship and the possibility of interference most especially. Such a diagram, while admittedly rather vague and susceptible of varying interpretations, seems to apply particularly to road traffic, and set it apart from other physical systems. It furnishes a valuable criterion of the success of any theory of road traffic, for a theory independent of or incompatible with the fundamental diagram cannot be considered correct.

Nevertheless, it would be a mistake to suppose that any one particular $\rho - \lambda$ diagram will apply in all situations. It is characteristic of a particular place at a particular time with a particular population of drivers. Any one of a number of events could change its form: changing visibility at twilight, a sudden fall of rain, or even the appearance of a police car.

In the best of circumstances, it might be possible to assume the road perfectly homogeneous. Then the fundamental diagram would be the same for different parts of the road and might indeed characterize the whole road. In this case the traffic engineer's concept of capacity as the maximum value of ρ would be more meaningful. But if the road varies from point to point, there could easily be a different value for the maximum of ρ for each point. The capacity of the road would then have to be defined as the least capacity of any point. This leads to a minimax type definition: capacity of a piece of road is the least value of all maximum ρ. We shall return to this question after deriving several $\rho - \lambda$ diagrams.

3.3 Statistical Deduction of Fundamental Diagram

Although the importance of the flow density diagram has been realized for some time, and certain (conflicting) empirical evidence regarding its shape occurs in the literature of traffic engineering, it is only recently that attempts have been made to deduce a functional form for it. If such an equation were well established, many important questions relating to flow and capacity could be reduced to estimation of constants.

It might even be possible to relate such constants to actual geometric properties of road segments. It is a testimony to the undeveloped state of road theory that even this modest proposal seems at present to be very difficult to realize. Only two proposals have been put forward to characterize the passibility of a road numerically, one of which will be mentioned in Section 7.8. (The other consists of assigning empirical numbers to every hill, curve, grade, bush, bump, etc., and is not likely to be useful.)

Suppose we assume that each car will travel at a constant speed x whenever it is free from interference from other cars, and that these *free speeds* are subject to some probability distribution

$$F(z) = \text{Prob}\,(x \leqslant z)$$

with density function

$$f(z) = (d/dz)\,F(z). \tag{1}$$

Suppose further that the distribution of free speeds has mean value $m_0 < \infty$ and variance $v_0 < \infty$. In the course of a journey, a car with free speed x will encounter interference from other cars and therefore be unable to maintain the speed x at all times. Denote his over-all average speed by the letter y, and suppose y to be a function of x and the traffic density λ.

The nature of the function $y = y(x, \lambda)$ is not easy to determine; in fact this is the central problem of Chapter 7. In the present chapter we will make some plausible statistical assumptions regarding the distribution of the random variables x and y, which are connected by the unknown transformation $y = y(x, \lambda)$; first, however, we give some examples of suitable $y(x, \lambda)$ functions. Such a function must satisfy simple boundary conditions: $y(x, 0) = x$, since a car may travel at free speed in the absence of traffic, and $y(x, \lambda') = 0$, since every car stops in a jam. Furthermore $y(0, \lambda) = 0$; this expresses the ability of a car to stop if it wishes. In the following examples, we normalize all speeds relative to m_0[†] and show functions which satisfy the boundary conditions.

EXAMPLE 1.

$$y = \log \frac{\lambda' e^x}{\lambda e^x + \lambda' - \lambda} \tag{2}$$

EXAMPLE 2.

$$y = \frac{\lambda' - \lambda}{\lambda} \arctan \frac{\lambda x}{\lambda' - \lambda}. \tag{3}$$

As pointed out in the preceding section, the correct domain of definition for x is $(0, \infty)$; this does not require that any particular driver will wish to remain stationary or travel infinitely fast. The choice of the real line for the domain of free speeds merely reflects the fact that there is no "natural" way of truncating the domain.

Such, however, is not the case for the variable y, for there is some maximum average speed approached as the free speed increases. We denote this function of λ by

$$L(\lambda) = y(\infty, \lambda)$$

[†] So that x and y are now dimensionless.

and note that $L(\lambda)$, also dimensionless, satisfies the conditions $L(0) = \infty$ and $L(\lambda') = 0$, corresponding to the freedom of an infinitely fast driver alone on the road and his constraint to immobility in a jam.

Statistically, we are looking for some convenient density function for y which is defined over $(0, L)$, and which has the limiting property of approaching a density defined over $(0, \infty)$ as λ approaches zero. This is a well known property of the Type I distribution (cf. Section 1.6)

$$C\, z^{\alpha-1} (L-z)^{L\beta-1}, \qquad 0 < z < L \tag{4}$$

where C is given by

$$C\, B(\alpha, L\beta)\, L^{L\beta+\alpha-1} = 1$$

and α and β are parameters. As $\lambda \to \lambda'$, $L \to 0$, and the mean and variance of y, given by

$$E(y) = m(\lambda) = \frac{\alpha L}{\beta L + \alpha} \tag{5}$$

and

$$\text{var}(y) = v(\lambda) = \frac{\alpha \beta L^3}{(\alpha + \beta L)^2(\alpha + \beta L + 1)} \tag{6}$$

both approach zero with L. This expresses the fact that in jam-packed traffic both the mean and variance of the speed distribution are zero.

In case of very light traffic $\lambda \to 0$, $L \to \infty$, and (4) approaches a Type III distribution

$$f(z) = C'\, z^{\alpha_0} e^{-\beta_0 z}, \qquad 0 < z < \infty \tag{7}$$

where C' is given by

$$C'\, \Gamma(\alpha_0) = \beta_0^{\alpha_0}$$

and α_0 and β_0 represent the limiting values of α and β in case these parameters are also functions of λ. This distribution for the variable x has the properties required for free speeds. The domain is the whole real line, and the mean and variance are given by

$$m_0 = \alpha_0/\beta_0, \qquad v_0 = \alpha_0/\beta_0^2.$$

By virtue of Eq. (5) the problem of determining a functional form for the fundamental diagram is reduced to the problem of finding the average speed of an infinitely fast car as a function of traffic density.

EXAMPLE 1. $L = \log (\lambda'/\lambda)$ and therefore (removing the normalization to m_0)

$$m(\lambda) = \frac{\alpha\, m_0 \log (\lambda'/\lambda)}{\beta \log (\lambda'/\lambda) + \alpha} \tag{8}$$

for some suitable constants α and β.

EXAMPLE 2. $L = \tfrac{1}{2}\pi \dfrac{\lambda' - \lambda}{\lambda}$, leading to

$$m(\lambda) = \frac{A(\lambda' - \lambda)}{B\lambda' + C\lambda} \tag{9}$$

for suitable constants A, B, and C.

It will be noticed that both these $m(\lambda)$ satisfy the boundary values: $m(\lambda') = 0$, $m(0) = m_0$.

So far, nothing has been said about the manner in which the speed measurements are performed. The time-space question has thus been left in the background. As we shall see in Chapter 4, time measured and space measured speed distributions are not identical, nor are their means. However, the mean of the space measured speed distribution is equal to the harmonic mean of the time measured speed distribution. Consequently it may be better for some purposes to replace (5) by the harmonic mean of (4). This can be shown to be equivalent to replacing α by $(\alpha - 1)$ in (5) and (8).

3.4 Car Following Deduction of Fundamental Diagram

The assumptions on which Section 3.3 were based, although reasonable, did not refer in any specific way to the interaction between cars. On the contrary, they were almost purely statistical, and involved traffic ideas only in the choice of appropriate statistical functions.

Now we obtain the fundamental diagram by microscopic consideration of two particular cars, one of which is assumed to be following the other. The price paid for this detail is very great: cars cannot pass one another. Consequently the results are most nearly valid for the region nearby λ', and in situations such as tunnels, where passing is explicitly forbidden.

The method of "car following" is psychological conjecture supported by empirical verification. It is assumed that each car follows its leader in a purely deterministic way which can be expressed by a certain differential equation. The differential equation is simply guessed at; the resulting flow-density diagram is then compared with data.

In such a situation, it is natural that increased refinement of instrumentation and quantity of evidence will test each conjecture more and more severely, so that a more elaborate differential equation will be needed. Moreover, it may be desirable to assume different following behavior for dense and sparse traffic, and this leads to two functional forms for the fundamental diagram, with the possibility of a discontinuity between them. At present the evidence is not conclusive on this point. There is certainly a considerable body of opinion which maintains the existence of the discontinuity, and therefore classifies the traffic stream as "freely flowing" or "congested." However, as we shall see, car following theory does not specify the location of the boundary.

Let the cars in a single lane be numbered consecutively beginning with the leading car, and let $x_n(t)$ denote the position of the nth car at time t, $x_n'(t)$ its velocity, and $x_n''(t)$ its acceleration. Although a large number of differential difference relations have been proposed, we shall concentrate on three basic equations which can be plausibly deduced and which yield specific flow-concentration relationships.

The California authorities recommend a minimum spacing between consecutive cars which is proportional to the velocity of the following car. Taking into account a car length, so that the same coordinate point of each car is specified, the rule can be written,

$$x_{n+1} = C(x_n - x_{n+1}) + k,$$

which it is convenient to represent in terms of acceleration as

$$x''_{n+1} = C(x_n' - x'_{n+1}).\qquad(1)$$

Equation (1) does not involve the distance between cars, and a more sophisticated model can be obtained by regarding C as the sensitivity of response, which is supposed to be inversely proportional to spacing, giving

$$x''_{n+1} = C\,\frac{x_n' - x'_{n+1}}{x_n - x_{n+1}}\qquad(2)$$

It can be argued still further that the sensitivity in Eq. (2) should be inversely proportional to headway, since the driver of the $(n + 1)$st car will be more alert with smaller headway than with greater headway. The headway of the $(n + 1)$st car is

$$\frac{x_n - x_{n+1}}{x'_{n+1}}$$

Therefore, this new conjecture leads to the equation

$$x''_{n+1} = C\,x'_{n+1}\,\frac{x_n' - x'_{n+1}}{(x_n - x_{n+1})^2}\qquad(3)$$

Since the fundamental relation which we are trying to obtain contains a velocity (or mean velocity), it is only necessary to integrate Eqs. (1), (2), and (3) once. As a matter of fact, for Eq. (1), the answer comes directly from the California rule; the differentiation of this rule served only the purpose of suggesting generalizations (2) and (3).

However, some very strong equilibrium assumptions are necessary, namely that each car finally assumes exactly the same speed and spacing as every other, so that individual values can safely be replaced by population means.

Equations (1), (2), and (3) yield, respectively,

$$x'_{n+1} = C\,(x_n - x_{n+1}) + k,\qquad(4)$$

$$x'_{n+1} = C\log(x_n - x_{n+1}) + k,\qquad(5)$$

and

$$\log x'_{n+1} = - C (x_n - x_{n+1})^{-1} + k, \qquad (6)$$

or, in equilibrium,

$$m = C/\lambda + k, \qquad (7)$$

$$m = C \log (1/\lambda) + k, \qquad (8)$$

$$\log m = - C \lambda + k. \qquad (9)$$

Since there are two boundary conditions available, $m(0) = 0$ and $m(\lambda') = 0$, it should be possible to evaluate both C and k. However, an examination of (7), (8), and (9) shows that the first two cannot be valid near $\lambda = 0$ and the third cannot be valid near $\lambda = \lambda'$. Therefore, we restrict (7) and (8) to dense traffic and (9) to sparse traffic and evaluate k at the appropriate boundary. Multiplying by λ, we find for the three car following postulates, the following flow-concentration curves:

$$\rho = C (1 - \lambda/\lambda') \qquad (10)$$

from Eq. (7),

$$\rho = C \lambda \log (\lambda'/\lambda) \qquad (11)$$

from Eq. (8), and

$$\rho = m_0 \lambda e^{-C\lambda} \qquad (12)$$

from Eq. (9). Notice that in Eq. (10), C is a flow rate, in Eq. (11) it is a velocity and in Eq. (12) it is a spacing, consistent with Eqs. (1), (2), and (3).

3.5 Fluid Analogy Deduction of Fundamental Diagram

If we assume ρ and u to depend (for position x and time t) only on the value of λ, Eq. (2) of Section 3.2 can be differentiated to yield

$$\frac{d\rho}{d\lambda} = \lambda \frac{du}{d\lambda} + u \qquad (1)$$

Suppose the cars to be analogous to a compressible fluid susceptible to shock waves. Then $d\rho/d\lambda$ is the speed of a shock wave, and

$$\frac{d\rho}{d\lambda} - u = C \tag{2}$$

expresses the hypothesis that the speed of a shock wave relative to the speed of the traffic fluid is constant. Substituting this into Eq. (1), we obtain the differential equation

$$\lambda \frac{du}{d\lambda} = C \tag{3}$$

with solution

$$u = C \log (\lambda'/\lambda). \tag{4}$$

This value corresponds, for $m = E(u)$, to the flow density diagram of Eq. (11), Section 3.4. An argument in support of Eq. (2) is that this equation represents only a moving coordinate system in which the velocity of a shock wave is measured, a fact undeniably applicable to true fluids on which the traffic analogy is based. The significance of the hydrodynamic analogy will be explained more fully in Section 4.10.

3.6 Experimentally Obtained Forms for Fundamental Diagram

There are two forms for the fundamental diagram which have been suggested by experimental data without the intervention of any theoretical considerations whatsoever. The first of these is based on a linear relationship between mean speed and traffic density. With parameters m_0 and λ', we have

$$\frac{m}{m_0} + \frac{\lambda}{\lambda'} = 1 \tag{1}$$

which leads to

$$\rho = \lambda m_0 \left(1 - \frac{\lambda}{\lambda'}\right). \tag{2}$$

The second empirical curve which has been obtained is

$$\rho = \frac{m_0 \, \lambda \, (\lambda' - \lambda)^{1/2}}{A \, m_0 \, \lambda^2 + (\lambda' - \lambda)^{1/2}} \, . \tag{3}$$

3.7 Comparison of Flow Density Relationships

It must be strongly emphasized at the outset that various forms for the fundamental diagram, which have been obtained in Sections 3.3, 3.4, and 3.5 are conjectural. Not one of them is sufficiently well based on the geometry and dynamics of vehicular traffic to be considered proven. Further, it is doubtful whether such a proof, with all the ambiguity and complexity of vehicular traffic will ever exist. It is much more in the spirit of empirical science that plausible conjectures will be rigorously tested by the methods of statistical inference, and accepted or rejected according to the extent to which they satisfy standard tests of statistical significance.

In the meanwhile, it is interesting to see to what extent the various conjectures are consistent with some traffic theoretic concepts which have been formulated. We begin by examining the agreement with boundary value postulates; the value of ρ should be zero for both $\lambda = 0$ and $\lambda = \lambda'$, and the value of m should be zero at $\lambda = \lambda'$ and m_0 at $\lambda = 0$. Table I shows the degree of agreement.

Next we turn to the question of capacity. It is by no means certain that the idea of capacity, as applied to a road, is useful or even meaningful. Some doubts have been shed on this concept by the arguments of Section 3.1; still others arise from contemplating the abundance of pejorative adjectives[†] which have been inflicted on it by traffic engineers.

Nevertheless, it will certainly be appropriate to investigate the relationships which exist between the parameters in hypothetical

---

[†] For example, "actual," "real," "possible," "effective," "nominal," "inherent," "practical," "potential," and various combinations of these.

TABLE I

Case	Equation	Proof and reference	Value of ρ		Value of m		Parameter constraints
			$\lambda = 0$	$\lambda = \lambda'$	$\lambda = 0$	$\lambda = \lambda'$	
I	$\rho = C\left(1 - \dfrac{\lambda}{\lambda'}\right)$	Car following; Eq. (10), Section 3.4	No	Yes	No	Yes	None
II	$\rho = C\lambda.\log(\lambda'/\lambda)$	Car following; Eq. (11), Section 3.4. Fluid Analogy; Eq. (4), Section 3.5	Yes	Yes	No	Yes	$C = optimum\ speed$
III	$\rho = m_0 \lambda e^{-C\lambda}$	Car following; Eq. (12), Section 3.4	Yes	No	Yes	No	$C = optimum\ headway$
IV	$\rho = \dfrac{m_0 \lambda \alpha \log(\lambda'/\lambda)}{\beta \log(\lambda'/\lambda) + \alpha}$	Statistical; Eq. (8), Section 3.3	Yes	Yes	Yes	Yes	$\alpha = \beta$ (α and β vanish)
V	$\rho = \dfrac{A\lambda(\lambda' - \lambda)}{B\lambda' + C\lambda}$	Statistical; Eq. (9), Section 3.3	Yes	Yes	Yes	Yes	$A = Bm_0$
VI	$\rho = \lambda m_0\left(1 - \dfrac{\lambda}{\lambda'}\right)$	Empirical; Eq. (2), Section 3.6	Yes	Yes	Yes	Yes	None
VII	$\rho = \dfrac{\lambda m_0(\lambda' - \lambda)^{1/2}}{Am_0\lambda^2 + (\lambda' - \lambda)^{1/2}}$	Empirical; Eq. (3), Section 3.6	Yes	Yes	Yes	Yes	None

flow density diagrams and maximal values of ρ. We use a subscript c to indicate values corresponding to $d\rho/d\lambda = 0$. Since ρ_c does not exist in Case I, we begin with Case II. Differentiation of the flow density equation yields

$$\frac{d\rho}{d\lambda} = -C + C \log{(\lambda'/\lambda)}$$

Setting this equal to zero, we have

$$\lambda' = e\lambda_c \tag{1}$$

from which we obtain

$$m_c = C \tag{2}$$

as indicated in the last column of Table I.

In Case III, there is also a unique maximum, satisfying

$$\lambda_c = 1/C \tag{3}$$

as shown in Table I, and

$$em_c = m_0. \tag{4}$$

Case IV is a little more interesting, yielding the equation

$$\lambda_c = \lambda' e^{-\omega}, \tag{5}$$

where

$$\omega^2 + \omega - 1 = 0. \tag{6}$$

The quadratic has exactly one positive root (~ 0.618) which gives a value for λ_c. A simple calculation shows that the optimal mean speed m_c satisfies

$$1/m_c = 1/m_0 + 1/\omega. \tag{7}$$

Case III can be obtained from Case IV by setting $\beta = 0$, and supplying a constant. Equation (5) of Section 3.3 shows that this is equivalent to supposing that the mean speed is the same as that of an infinitely fast driver, which certainly makes sense when we remember that Case III was obtained under the assumption that passing is prohibited. Moreover, if we set $\beta = 0$ in Eq. (5), the result is exactly Eq. (1), and Eq. (2) is also satisfied. This suggests that the speed distribution in car following may be the degenerate density

$$L^{1-\alpha} \frac{z^{\alpha-1}}{L-z}, \qquad 0 < z < \mathrm{L}. \tag{8}$$

Equation (8) cannot define a proper density function, for its area is infinite, due to the slow approach to the asymptote $z = L$. However, it could be made acceptable by either truncating just short of L, or else by taking β just slightly greater than zero.

Case V also leads to a quadratic with a single positive root, namely

$$C\lambda_c^2 + 2\lambda' \lambda_c B - B\lambda'^2 = 0. \tag{9}$$

Since Case VI is a parabola, the optimum concentration is half the jam concentration, and this fact can easily be deduced from Eq. (3) of Section 3.6. Note that Case VI can be obtained from Case V by setting $C = 0$.

In Case VII, differentiation and simplification shows that λ_c satisfies

$$A \, m_0 \, \lambda_c^2(2\lambda' - \lambda_c) = 2(\lambda' - \lambda_c)^{3/2}, \tag{10}$$

essentially a sixth degree polynomial in λ_c.

There is one startling difference between the capacity values for Cases II, III, IV, and VI on one hand and Cases V and VII on the other: the former are absolutely independent of road parameters. In fact Case VI implies strictly that capacity is obtained at half jam, Cace II that capacity is at 37% of jam, and Case IV that capacity is at 54% of jam. Such results quite clearly violate common sense since they provide no way of taking into consideration hills, curves, day or night, width of roadway, etc., to say nothing of driver parameters. Case III, while not so obviously absurd on capacity, is nevertheless rather queer, since it requires the mean speed to be 37% of the desired mean speed for capacity flow. No doubt the driver's desire is now taken into consideration, and hopefully we may suppose that each driver makes his own evaluation of the road parameters.

In Cases V and VII, the optimal values are expressed in terms of statistical parameters which would take on different values with different roads and different driver populations.

3.8 Car Following for Cases IV, V, VI, and VII

In making use of the differential equations of car following, the simple substitutions $x'_{n+1} = m$ and $x_n - x_{n+1} = 1/\lambda$ provide the key to the technique, although several theoretical justifications should be supplied. The same procedure is easy to reverse, giving another (at least intuitive) test for flow density diagrams which might be obtained in some other way. For example, since the equation $m = m(\lambda)$ should pass through the point m_0 on the m-axis and the point λ' on the λ-axis, and since it is quite reasonable to expect slope zero and infinity respectively at these two points, a seemingly sensible conjecture would be the ellipse

$$\frac{\lambda^2}{\lambda'^2} + \frac{m^2}{m_0^2} = 1. \tag{1}$$

Differentiating with respect to t, we obtain

$$\frac{\lambda}{\lambda'^2}\frac{d\lambda}{dt} + \frac{m}{m_0^2}\frac{dm}{dt} = 0 \tag{2}$$

or in terms of dynamic variables

$$-\frac{1}{\lambda'^2}\frac{1}{x_n - x_{n+1}}\frac{x'_n - x'_{n+1}}{(x_n - x_{n+1})^2} + \frac{x'_{n+1}x''_{n+1}}{m_0^2} = 0, \tag{3}$$

which leads to the car following postulate

$$x''_{n+1} = C\frac{x'_n - x'_{n+1}}{(x_n - x_{n+1})^3}\frac{1}{x'_{n+1}}. \tag{4}$$

We can now summarize several car following postulates in simple terms.

Case I: Acceleration $\sim$ relative speed

Case II: Acceleration $\sim$ (relative speed)(spacing)$^{-1}$

Case III: Acceleration $\sim$ (relative speed)(spacing)$^{-1}$(headway)$^{-1}$

Ellipse: Acceleration $\sim$ (relative speed)(spacing)$^{-3}$(speed)$^{-1}$,

and perhaps invent sensible new cases such as

Hyperbola: Acceleration $\sim$ (relative speed)(headway)$^{-1}$

To see that the hyperbola $m = C/\lambda$ does arise from the last case, it is sufficient to integrate

$$\frac{x''_{n+1}}{x'_{n+1}} = \frac{x_n' - x'_{n+1}}{x_n - x_{n+1}}. \tag{5}$$

In particular, we wish to see how Cases IV–VII fit in with car following. In Case IV we first note that

$$\omega = \log \lambda'(x_n - x_{n+1}) \tag{6}$$

is the log of spacing measured in car lengths, and that

$$\frac{d\omega}{d\lambda} = -\frac{1}{\lambda}. \tag{7}$$

Differentiating Eq. (8) of Section 3.3, we obtain

$$x''_{n+1} = \frac{dm}{dt} = \frac{dm}{d\lambda}\frac{d\lambda}{dt} = -\frac{x_n' - x'_{n+1}}{(x_n - x_{n+1})^2}\frac{dm}{d\lambda}$$

$$x''_{n+1} = m_0 \frac{x_n' - x'_{n+1}}{x_n - x_{n+1}} \frac{1}{[\log \lambda'(x_n - x_{n+1})]^2}. \tag{8}$$

This represents a slight modification of Case II. It is not difficult to treat Cases V and VI similarly, obtaining

$$x''_{n+1} = -\frac{x_n' - x'_{n+1}}{k(x_n - x_{n+1})^2 + C} \tag{9}$$

for Case V and

$$x''_{n+1} = \frac{m_0}{\lambda'} \frac{x_n' - x'_{n+1}}{(x_n - x_{n+1})^2} \tag{10}$$

for Case VI. These cases are also similar from the point of view of car following:

Cases V and VI: Acceleration $\sim$ (relative speed) (spacing)$^{-2}$.

The car following equation for Case VII is the most complicated:

$$x_{n+1}'' = \tfrac{1}{2}A\,(x_{n+1}')^2\,\frac{4\lambda'(x_n - x_{n+1})^3 - 3(x_n - x_{n+1})^2}{[\lambda'(x_n - x_{n+1})^4 - (x_n - x_{n+1})^3]^{3/2}}. \quad (11)$$

Equation (11) is fairly sensible with respect to spacing, since it is essentially of degree -3 in $(x_n - x_{n+1})$. However the presence of squared velocity in the numerator is not really desirable. If we combine two of the spacing factors with these velocities, we can write

Case VII: Acceleration $\sim$ (headway)$^{-2}$ (spacing)$^{-1}$

and note that the relative speed of the two cars does not occur.

3.9 A Fifth Boundary Condition

Consider an absolutely empty road, $\lambda = 0$. The assumption which has been made, that there exists a mean free speed m_0 at this point is surely more properly expressed as a limit

$$\lim_{\lambda \to 0} m(\lambda) = m_0.$$

But the existence of such a limit is more a matter of common sense than of mathematical demonstration or even empirical verification. We now propose to extend the conjecture and assume that

$$\lim_{\lambda \to 0} \frac{dm}{d\lambda} = 0, \quad (1)$$

thereby stating that the addition of a small amount of traffic to an empty system will hardly depress the mean speed from the hypothetical value m_0. This boundary condition is by no means so obvious as the other four. It is impossible to imagine a system in which the previous conditions are denied. Equation (1), on the other hand, although appealing in its present form, could conceivably be replaced by

$$\lim_{\lambda \to 0} \frac{dm}{d\lambda} = \varepsilon, \tag{2}$$

where ε is a small quantity.

The most remarkable aspect of Eq. (1) is that, if true, it destroys every preceding form for the Fundamental Diagram, with the exception of Case VII. Cases I, II, and IV come off especially badly, since they yield an infinite slope at low density; Cases III, V, and VI at least satisfy Eq. (2). Table II summarizes the relative merits of the various cases from several points of view.

TABLE II

Case	Sensible car following equation	Suitable definition of capacity	Satisfies conditions (1) – (4)	$\dfrac{dm}{d\lambda}$	Satisfies condition (5)
I	(Derived from car following)	Meaningless	No	$-\dfrac{C}{\lambda^2}$	No
II	(Derived from car following)	No	No	$-\dfrac{C}{\lambda}$	No
III	(Derived from car following)	Possibly	No	$-C\,m_0\,e^{-C\lambda}$	Partially
IV	Yes	No	Yes	$-\dfrac{m_0}{\lambda}\dfrac{1}{[1 + \log(\lambda'/\lambda)]^2}$	No
V	Yes	Yes	Yes	$-Bm_0\,\lambda'\dfrac{B+C}{(B\lambda' + C\lambda)^2}$	Partially
VI	Yes	No	Yes	$-\dfrac{m_0}{\lambda'}$	Partially
VII	Possibly	Yes	Yes	$-A\,m^2\,\lambda(2\lambda' - \lambda)(\lambda' - \lambda)^{1/2}$	Yes

3.10 Comment

The relationship between density of traffic and traffic flow is one which has engaged the interest of traffic engineers for many years, and consequently the literature of traffic engineering contains much empirical data on the question. As typical examples, we mention the work of Creighton [5], Wardrop [41, 42, 42a], Forbes [11] and Greenshields [14], although a large bibliography could be compiled on this subject alone. Linear $m - \lambda$ (Case VI) has been especially popular, and was apparently first proposed by Greenshields [51]. Case VII although suggested[†] by Guerin [54] and Palmer [55] to fit data, nevertheless appealed to them because of its advantages with respect to the fifth boundary condition, a property of which they are well aware.

The question of road capacity has also been extensively investigated by the traffic engineering profession, but without general agreement on either the definition of the concept, or on methods for measuring it. In this connection, we mention the book of Hess [21] and papers of Wardrop [40, 42] and Barnes [1]. Many other empirical and semi-empirical works on capacity have appeared, and may be found in journals such as *Public Roads*, *Traffic Engineering*, in publications of the Highway Research Board, and in the Highway Capacity Manual [53].

The statistical approach (Cases IV and V) to volume density relationships is due to Haight [15, 16].

Although dynamical considerations in car following are implicit in the early paper of Herrey and Herrey [20], the first genuine car following model is due to Reuschel [36, 37]. Of the specific models treated here, Case I is due to Pipes [34], Case II to Gazis *et al.* [12] and Case III to Edie [8]. Kometani and Sasaki [23] deduce an equation involving the acceleration of both leading and following drivers from a very intricate argument regarding driving behavior. Herman *et al.* [18] introduce the velocity of the two   nearest

---

[†] In the context of travel time, $1/m$.

neighbors into the driver's calculations. Gazis *et al.* [*44*] discuss a generalization of Eq. (3), Section 3.4, in which both x'_{n+1} and $(x_n - x_{n+1})$ are raised to arbitrary powers, and show how these exponents occur in the Fundamental Diagram. Parallel lanes of traffic going in the same direction are treated by Gazis and Herman [*48*] under the assumption of interacting car following equations. Newell [*29*] proposes a very general model involving arbitrary differential difference operators and obtains some approximations for special cases. Recently, Newell [*47*] suggests separate car following policies for accelerating and decelerating cars.

Many authors recognize the need to introduce a time lag into the car following equation. Chandler, Herman, and Montroll put such a lag into Pipes' Eq. (1) Section 3.4, and Chow [*4*] solves the resulting equation. It appears that Chow's solution (given by Montroll [*46*] in compact form) is the only complete result for a car following equation with lag. However Herman *et al.* [*18*] give a very good analysis of Pipes' equation with lag as the traffic stream approaches stability. Sasaki [*39*] and Kometani and Sasaki [*22, 49*] have also investigated this question.

Car following equations are purely deterministic, so that the motion of the first car in line must determine exactly the behavior of every following car. Pipes [*34*] considers infinite acceleration, constant acceleration and exponential acceleration as well as various types of deceleration including the sudden stop. Kometani and Sasaki [*24, 25*] permit the leading driver to vary his speed in the form of a periodic wave. Many other authors (cf. Montroll [*46*]) give results of this type.

A further question of interest in car following theory is the rear end collision. The linked difference equations can, for certain parameter values, produce impossible deceleration values for the *n*th car by means of very moderate perturbations in the velocity of the first car. Kometani and Sasaki [*23*] use these equations to develop a "safety index," and Herman *et al.* [*18*] illustrate values of the constants which can lead very quickly to a collision.

Since the model defined by Case II satisfies both boundary conditions for high density, and that defined by Case III satisfies both boundary conditions for low density, Edie [8] argues that these two equations could be used jointly, with a discontinuity between them corresponding to the break between freely flowing and congested traffic. There appears to be no general agreement on when (if ever) there is such a discontinuity, although there is some evidence to support either side of the question. Some interesting arguments on this point are produced by Gazis, Herman, and Rothery [44], who also comment very cogently on Edie's paper.

Oliver[†] points out that Eq. (4) of Section 3.2 represents in the $\lambda - \rho - m$ space a surface in general, and yet the traffic theoretic interpretation requires the locus to be a skew curve. He believes that some difficulty may arise from the omission of position and time from the arguments in this equation, and that the locus may properly be a surface for small λ and a skew curve for large λ.

Vehicular tunnels form a perfect laboratory for testing car following theories, and a considerable amount of work has been done in the tunnels of the Port of New York Authority. Although the relationship between following policy and roadway characteristics[‡] has been well elucidated, the evidence in favor of any one particular flow density relation does not appear conclusive. In this connection, we mention the work of Edie [7, 9, 10], Helly [17], Herman and Potts [19], and Olcott [31]. The best recent report on empirical fit to car following theory is given by Gazis et al. [44]. Greenberg and Daou [50] show how results of this kind can be put to practical use.

The hydrodynamic analogy was developed simultaneously by Lighthill and Whitham [26, 27] and Richards [38]. Although the two approaches are superficially rather different, Pipes [32] has shown them to be identical. Generalizations of the Lighthill-Whitham-Richards theory have been given by De [6] and Bick and Newell [2]. The specific form for the flow density relationship which we have called Case II is derived by Greenberg [13], using a

---

[†] In private correspondence.
[‡] For example, gradient and distance from exit.

more complicated argument than given here. Greenberg employs the equation of continuity of matter, $\lambda_t + \rho_x = 0$, as well as an equation for the flow of a one dimensional fluid, $\lambda(du/dt) = -C\,\lambda_x$.

Hydrodynamic models and car following models have in common the prediction of shock waves in traffic, and a substantial part of the work, both theoretical and practical, has been oriented in this direction. As we have noted, the slope of the Fundamental Diagram is equal to the wave velocity, and the slope of a radius vector to this diagram is the fluid velocity. This constraint enables one to predict shock wave formation and velocity from the diagram, or, conversely, to obtain the diagram from observed waves. Since observable waves travel backwards in traffic, the predictions must be limited arbitrarily to congested traffic, although Pipes [32] states that the theory is equally consistent with forward waves.

The expression *traffic dynamics* is now often used to describe car following and fluid flow models collectively. The subject has much wider significance than would be suggested by the present chapter and it is to be hoped that the present volume will soon be complemented by a work in which road traffic is systematically explained in terms of traffic dynamics. A good introductory study of this important subject is due to Oliver [57].

REFERENCES

1. Barnes, H. A., Engineering Studies of Urban Traffic Flow. *Operations Research* **3**, No. 4, 536–44 (Nov. 1955).
2. Bick, J. H., and Newell, G. F., A Continuum Model for Traffic Flow on an Undivided Highway. *Quarterly Appl. Math.* **18**, No. 2, 191–204 (1960).
3. Chandler, R. E., Herman, R., and Montroll, E. W., Traffic Dynamics: Studies in Car Following. *Operations Research* **6**, 165–84 (1958).
4. Chow, Tse-Sun, Operational Analysis of a Traffic-Dynamics Problem. *Operations Research* **6**, No. 6, 827–34 (Nov.-Dec. 1958).
5. Creighton, R. L., Speed Volume Relationships on Signalized Roads. *Chicago Area Transportation Study Research News* **1**, No. 11, 6–11 (June 1957).
6. De, S. C., Kinematic Wave Theory of Bottlenecks of Varying Capacity. *Proc. Cambridge Phil. Soc.* **52**, Part 3, 564–72 (July 1956).

7. Edie, L. C., Experiments in Single Lane Flow in Tunnels. *In* Herman, R. (ed.), "Theory of Traffic Flow," pp. 175–192 Proceedings of the Symposium on the Theory of Traffic Flow, held at the General Motors Research Laboratories, Warren, Michigan. Elsevier, Amsterdam, 1961.

8. Edie, L. C., Car-Following and Steady-State Theory for Noncongested Traffic. *Operations Research* **9**, No. 1, 66–76 (Jan.-Feb. 1961).

9. Edie, L. C., and Foote, R. S., Effect of Shock Waves on Tunnel Traffic Flow. *Proc. Highway Research Board* **39**, 492–505 (1960).

10. Edie, L. C., and Foote, R. S., Traffic Flow in Tunnels. *Proc. Highway Research Board* **37**, 334–44 (1958).

11. Forbes, T. W., Speed, Headway and Volume Relationships on a Freeway. *Proc. Inst. Traffic Engrs.* **22**, 103–26 (1951).

12. Gazis, D. C., Herman, R., and Potts, R. B., Car-Following Theory of Steady-State Traffic Flow. *Operations Research* **7**, No. 4, 499–505 (July-Aug. 1959).

13. Greenberg, H., An Analysis of Traffic Flow. *Operations Research* **7**, No. 1, 79–85 (Jan.-Feb. 1959).

14. Greenshields, B. D., The Density Factor in Traffic Flow. *Traffic Engineering* **30**, No. 6, 26–30 (March 1960).

15. Haight, F. A., Towards a Unified Theory of Road Traffic. *Operations Research* **6**, No. 6, 813–26 (Nov.-Dec. 1958).

16. Haight, F. A., The Volume, Density Relation in the Theory of Road Traffic. *Operations Research* **8**, No. 4, 572–73 (July-Aug. 1960).

17. Helly, W., Dynamics of Single Lane Vehicular Traffic Flow. Mass. Inst. Technol. Center for Operations Research, Research Report No. 2. Cambridge, Massachusetts, Oct., 1959.

18. Herman, R., Montroll, E. W., Potts, R. B., and Rothery, R. W., Traffic Dynamics: Analysis of Stability in Car Following. *Operations Research* **7**, No. 1, 86–106 (Jan.-Feb. 1959).

19. Herman, R., and Potts, R. B., Single Lane Traffic Theory and Experiment. *In* Herman, R. (ed.), "Theory of Traffic Flow," pp. 120–146. Proceedings of the Symposium on the Theory of Traffic Flow, held at the General Motors Research Laboratories, Warren, Michigan. Elsevier, Amsterdam, 1961.

20. Herrey, E. M. J., and Herrey, H., Principles of Physics Applied to Traffic Movements and Road Conditions. *Am. J. Phys.* **13**, 1–14 (1945).

21. Hess, V. F., "The Capacity of a Highway." New Haven Traffic Engineering, Institute of Traffic Engineers, New Haven, Connecticut, 1950.

22. Kometani, E., and Sasaki, T., On the Stability of Traffic Flow (Report I). *J. Operations Research Soc. Japan* **2**, No. 1, 11–26 (1958).

23. Kometani, E., and Sasaki, T., A Safety Index for Traffic with Linear Spacings. *Mem. Fac. Eng. Kyoto Univ.* **21**, Part 3, 229–46 (July 1959).

24. Kometani, E., and Sasaki, T., Dynamic Behavior of Traffic with Non-linear Spacing-Speed Relationship. *In* Herman, R. (ed.), "Theory of Traffic Flow," pp. 105–109. Proceedings of the Symposium on the Theory of Traffic Flow,

held at the General Motors Research Laboratories, Warren, Michigan. Elsevier, Amsterdam, 1961.

25. Kometani, E., and Sasaki, T., Traffic Dynamics. *Proc. 5th Japan Road Conference* (1959)

26. Lighthill, M. J., and Whitham, G. B., On Kinematic Waves; I. Flood Movement in Long Rivers. *Proc. Roy. Soc.*, Ser. A, **229**, 281–316 (1955).

27. Lighthill, M. J., and Whitham, G. B., On Kinematic Waves; II. A Theory of Traffic Flow on Long Crowded Roads. *Proc. Roy. Soc.* Ser. A, **229**, 317–45 (May 10, 1955).

28. Newell, G. F., A Theory of Platoon Formation in Tunnel Traffic. *Operations Research* **7**, No. 5, 589–98 (Sept.-Oct. 1959).

29. Newell, G. F., Nonlinear Effects in the Dynamics of Car Following. *Operations Research* **9**, No. 2, 209–29 (March-April 1961).

30. Newell, G. F., A Theory of Traffic Flow in Tunnels. *In* Herman, R. (ed.), "Theory of Traffic Flow," pp. 193–206. Proceedings of the Symposium on the Theory of Traffic Flow, held at the General Motors Research Laboratories, Warren, Michigan. Elsevier, Amsterdam, 1961.

31. Olcott, E. S., The Influence of Vehicular Speed and Spacing on Tunnel Capacity. *J. Operations Research Soc. Am.* **3**, 147–67 (1955).

32. Pipes, L. A., "A Comparison of the Lighthill-Whitham and the Richards Theory of Traffic Shock Waves" (unpublished).

33. Pipes, L. A., A Proposed Dynamic Analogy of Traffic. Univ. of California Institute of Transportation and Traffic Engineering Special Report, Los Angeles, California, July 1950.

34. Pipes, L. A., An Operational Analysis of Traffic Dynamics. *J. Appl. Phys.* **24**, 274–81 (1953).

35. Pipes, L. A., A Mathematical Analysis of Traffic Dynamics. *J. Operations Research Soc. Am.* **1**, 151 (1953). [Abstract of (*34*)].

36. Reuschel, A., Fahrzeugbewegungen in der Kolonne. *Österr. Ingr.-Arch.* **4** 193–215 (1950). (English summary.)

37. Reuschel, A., Fahrzeugbewegungen in der Kolonne bei gleichförmig beschleunigtem oder verzögertem Leitfahrzeug. *Z. Österr. Ing.-Arch.-Ver.* **95**, 59–62; 73–77 (1950).

38. Richards, P. I., Shock Waves on the Highway. *Operations Research* **4**, 42–51 (1956).

39. Sasaki, T., On the Stability of Traffic Flow (Report II). *J. Operations Research Soc. Japan* **2**, No. 2, 60–79 (1959).

40. Wardrop, J. G., The Capacity of Roads. *Operational Research Quar.* **5**, 14–21 (1954).

41. Wardrop, J. G., Some Theoretical Aspects of Road Traffic Research. *Proc. Inst. Civil Engrs. (London)* **1**, 325–62 (1952).

42. Wardrop, J. G., Traffic Capacity of Town Streets. *Roads and Road Construct.* **30**, No. 350, 39–42 (Feb. 1952).

42a. Wardrop, J. G., Traffic Capacity of Town Streets. *Roads and Road Construct.* **30**, No. 351, 68–71 (1952).

43. Woods, W. A., Dynamics of Halting a Line of Traffic. *Engineering* **191**, No. 4960, 655–56 (May 12, 1961).

44. Gazis, D. C., Herman, R., and Rothery, R. W., Nonlinear Follow-the-Leader Models of Traffic Flow. *Operations Research* **9**, No. 4, 545–567 (July-Aug. 1961).

45. Tuck, E., Stability of Following in Two Dimensions. *Operations Research* **9**, No. 4, 479–495 (July-Aug. 1961).

46. Montroll, E. W., On the Motion of Vehicular Traffic on Roads without Intersections (unpublished).

47. Newell, G. F., Theories of Instability in Dense Highway Traffic. *J. Operations Research (Japan)* (to appear).

48. Gazis, D. C., Herman, R., and Weiss, G. H., Density Oscillations between Lanes of a Multilane Highway. *Operations Research* **10**, 658–67 (1962).

49. Kometani, E., and Sasaki, T., Car Following Theory and Stability Limit of Traffic Volume. *J. Operations Research Soc. Japan* **3**, No. 4, 176–190 (March 1961).

50. Greenberg, H., and Daou, A., The Control of Traffic Flow to Increase the Flow. *Operations Research* **8**, No. 4, 524–532 (July-Aug. 1960).

51. Greenshields, B. D., A Study in Highway Capacity. *Proc. Highway Research Board* **14**, 448–477 (1934).

52. Miller, A. J., Sample Estimates of Flow-Concentration Curves (unpublished).

53. *Highway Capacity Manual*, Bureau of Public Roads. U. S. Government Printing Office, Washington, D. C., 1950.

54. Guerin, N. S., Travel Time Relationships. *In* Quality and Theory of Traffic Flow, pp. 71–103. Bureau of Highway Traffic, Yale University, New Haven, Connecticut, 1961.

55. Palmer, M. R. The Development of Traffic Congestion. *In* Quality and Theory of Traffic Flow, pp. 107–140. Bureau of Highway Traffic, Yale University, New Haven, Connecticut, 1961.

56. Underwood, R. T., Speed, Volume, and Density Relationships. *In* Quality and Theory of Traffic Flow, pp. 143–188. Bureau of Highway Traffic, Yale University, New Haven, Connecticut, 1961.

57. Oliver, R. M., Fluid Flow Models of Traffic Streams (mimeograph).

CHAPTER 4

Arrangement of Cars on a Road

4.1 Introduction

The positions of cars at a fixed moment, or the times of arrival of cars at a fixed place, form a stochastic process in space or time respectively. In this chapter, we consider four aspects of the process, namely:

A. Sensible generalizations of randomness, Sections 4.2–4.6.
B. The process in space and time, Sections 4.7–4.8.
C. Analogous mathematical theories, Sections 4.9–4.10.
D. Correlation between successive gaps, Section 4.11.

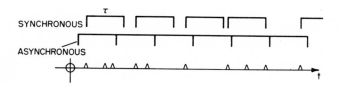

FIG. 10. Synchronous and asynchronous counting.

The term *arrangement* is supposed to include both the time process and the space process, and the analogous term *gap* to mean either *headway* between the same point on consecutive cars (for the time process) or *spacing* between the same point on consecutive cars (for the space process). Similarly, we will refer to the *time counting* distribution and *space counting* distribution.

It will also be necessary to introduce a distinction between methods of car counting. *Synchronous counting* begins just after a car passes (in time) or occurs (in space); *asynchronous counting* begins at an arbitrary point in time or space. We have seen that a random arrangement has no aging effect; therefore the synchronous and asynchronous counting distributions are the same, the Poisson. Since lack of aging in the gap distribution is also sufficient for randomness, every nonrandom arrangement must have distinct synchronous and asynchronous counting distributions. Figure 10 illustrates the difference between synchronous and asynchronous counting periods.

4.2 Starting Density

In the synchronous case, a count of n vehicles corresponds exactly to the elapse of n gaps, each of which has density $g(x)$. In the asynchronous case, $n - 1$ of these gaps have density $g(x)$, while the first has a density which we call the *starting density corresponding to* $g(x)$.

If the mean gap size is γ, and the cumulative distribution of gaps is $G(x)$, then the starting density is

$$g_0(x) = \frac{1 - G(x)}{\gamma}, \qquad 0 < x < \infty \qquad (1)$$

a fact which we now prove. Suppose the count begins a distance x before the end of a gap of length y. Then the distribution of $x|y$ is rectangular over $(0, y)$

$$1/y, \qquad 0 < x < y \qquad (2)$$

and of $y|x$ is $g(y)$ contracted to the domain (x, ∞), namely

$$\frac{g(y)}{1 - G(x)}, \qquad x < y < \infty. \qquad (3)$$

Substituting these two conditional distributions into Bayes Theorem, Eq. (3), Section 1.8, we obtain

$$(1/y)\, g_1(y) = \frac{g(y)}{1 - G(x)}\, g_0(x), \qquad (4)$$

where $g_1(y)$ is the density for the length of the interval surrounding an arbitrarily chosen point. Multiplying by y and integrating on y, we get Eq. (1).

For the random process, $\gamma = 1/\mu$, $G(x) = 1 - e^{-\mu x}$, and therefore $g_0(x) = \mu e^{-\mu x} = g(x)$, as we already know. For the Erlang process of Section 2.8, $\gamma = k/\mu$,

$$G(x) = \frac{\gamma(k, \mu x)}{\Gamma(k)},$$

[cf. Eq. (8) of Section 1.6] and therefore

$$g_0(x) = \frac{\mu}{k} \frac{\Gamma(k, \mu x)}{\Gamma(k)}. \tag{5}$$

Let the Laplace transforms of the density $g(x)$ and of the corresponding starting density $g_0(x)$ be $\phi(s)$ and $\phi_0(s)$ respectively. Then, using Eq. (1) with Eq. (4) of Section 1.9, it is easy to see that

$$\phi_0(s) = \frac{1 - \phi(s)}{\gamma s}. \tag{6}$$

Furthermore, if the nth central moment of $g(x)$ is m_n and the nth central moment of $g_0(x)$ is $m_n{}^0$, expansion of Eq. (6) yields

$$n \, m_1 \, m_{n-1}^0 = m_n. \tag{7}$$

The argument used in this section also gives the distribution of gap size in which an arbitrarily chosen point lies, namely the unconditional distribution of y. Substituting (1) into Eq. (4) we find that

$$g_1(x) = \frac{x \, g(x)}{\gamma}. \tag{8}$$

The formula for the moments of the starting up density can be used to prove the Pollaczek formula in queueing theory, Eq. (5), Section 2.7. If arrivals occur at random, the instant of arrival is an arbitrary moment in time with respect to the service process. Therefore the waiting time for such an arrival, before beginning service is the sum of the starting up mean and K service periods of length $(1/\mu)$, where K is the number queueing, excluding the one in service if any. Setting $n = 2$ in Eq. (7), we obtain

$$\frac{m_2}{2m_1} = \frac{\text{var}(v) + (1/\mu^2)}{2/\mu} \tag{9}$$

for the first of these quantities, conditional on service taking place. Since $\pi_0 = 1 - \rho$ for every queue with random arrivals [cf. Eqs. (6) and (7), Section 2.4], the expression (9) will be unconditional if multiplied by ρ. K is either the queue length or one less than the queue length, depending on whether the queue is empty or not, that is

$$K = \bar{u}(1 - \rho) + (\bar{u} - 1)\rho = \bar{u} - \rho. \tag{10}$$

Using the notation of Section 2.7, Eqs. (9) and (10) yield

$$\bar{w} = \rho \, \frac{\text{var}(v) + (1/\mu^2)}{2/\mu} + (1/\mu)(\bar{u} - \rho),$$

and since $\bar{u} = \rho + \lambda\bar{w}$ from Eq. (1) of Section 2.7, we obtain

$$\bar{u} = \rho + \tfrac{1}{2}\lambda^2 \left[\text{var}(v) + (1/\mu^2)\right] + \rho(\bar{u} - \rho). \tag{11}$$

Solving Eq. (11) for $\bar{u}$, we obtain the Pollaczek formula.

Furthermore, we have in this section obtained not only the mean value for starting up, but its distribution and Laplace transformation, so that the argument given above could be extended.

4.3 Gap-Counting Relationships

In this section we will use the notation and terminology of headway and time counting, but the argument can equally well be applied to spacing and space counting. Let the length of the counting period be τ, and the probability of recording n cars in time τ be $p_n(\tau)$, with cumulative form

$$P_n(\tau) = \text{Prob (cars counted in time } \tau \leqslant n) \tag{1}$$

$$= \text{Prob (sum of } n + 1 \text{ gaps} \geqslant \tau) \tag{2}$$

so that

$$P_n(\tau) = \int_\tau^\infty g^{(n+1)} * (x) \, dx \tag{3}$$

for the synchronous case. Let the corresponding quantities for an asynchronous counting period be $\bar{p}_n(t)$ and $\bar{P}_n(t)$. Then

$$\bar{P}_n(\tau) = \int_\tau^\infty g^{n*}(x) * g_0(x) \, dx \tag{4}$$

by the same argument where $g(x)$ is the gap density and $g_0(x)$ is the starting density.

SYNCHRONOUS CASE. The Laplace transform of $g^{(n+1)*}$ is ϕ^{n+1}, where ϕ is the Laplace transform of g. Therefore, the Laplace transform (with respect to τ) of

$$1 - P_n(\tau) = \int_0^\tau g^{(n+1)*}(x) \, dx \tag{5}$$

is $\phi^{n+1}(s)/s$. Hence, defining the tail of the synchronous counting distribution to be $Q_n(\tau) = 1 - P_n(\tau)$, we have

$$Q_n(\tau) = \text{Inverse Laplace transform of } \phi^{n+1}/s \tag{6}$$

which is convenient to write

$$Q_n(\tau) = \mathscr{L}^{-1} [\phi^{n+1}/s]. \tag{7}$$

Using this abbreviated notation, the generating function

$$\pi(z) = \sum p_n z^n$$

can be expressed as a simple function of ϕ. For

$$\pi(z) = 1 + \sum_1 Q_{n-1} z^n - \sum_0 Q_n z^n$$

$$= 1 + \sum_1 \mathscr{L}^{-1} \frac{\phi^n z^n}{s} - \sum_0 \mathscr{L}^{-1} \frac{\phi^{n+1} z^n}{s}$$

$$= 1 + \mathscr{L}^{-1} \frac{\phi z}{s(1 - \phi z)} - \mathscr{L}^{-1} \frac{\phi}{s(1 - \phi z)}. \tag{8}$$

Since the Laplace transform of unity is $1/s$, the terms of Eq. (8) can be combined to yield

$$\pi(z) = \mathscr{L}^{-1} \frac{1 - \phi}{s(1 - \phi z)}.$$ (9)

ASYNCHRONOUS CASE. Using Eq. (6) of Section 4.2, we see that the Laplace transform of $g^{n*} * g_0$ is $\phi^n(1 - \phi)/s\gamma$, and therefore

$$\bar{Q}_n(\tau) = \mathscr{L}^{-1} \frac{\phi^n(1 - \phi)}{s^2 \gamma}.$$ (10)

Equation (4) of Section 1.9 shows that one of the s in the denominator of Eq. (10) can be replaced by an incomplete integral. The remainder of the function corresponds exactly to Eq. (7), so that we can write

$$\bar{Q}_n(\tau) = \frac{1}{\gamma} \int_0^\tau (Q_{n-1} - Q_n)\, dt$$ (11)

$$= \frac{1}{\gamma} \int_0^\tau p_n(t)\, dt.$$ (12)

Following now the same argument as in the synchronous case, we find that the generating function $\bar{\pi}(z) = \Sigma \bar{p}_n z^n$ can be written

$$\bar{\pi}(z) = \mathscr{L}^{-1} \left[\frac{1}{s} + \frac{(1 - \phi)(z - 1)}{s^2 \gamma(1 - \phi z)} \right]$$ (13)

Either Eq. (9) and (13) or else Eq. (12) can be used to establish the following convenient relationships between the synchronous and asynchronous counting generating functions:

$$\frac{\bar{\pi}(z) - 1}{z - 1} = \frac{1}{\gamma} \int_0^\tau \pi(z)\, dt$$ (14)

and

$$\frac{d\bar{\pi}}{d\tau} = (z - 1) \frac{\pi(z)}{\gamma}.$$ (15)

We have not explicitly indicated the functional dependence of π and $\bar{\pi}$ on τ, although it is clearly implied by the dependence of p and $\bar{p}$ on the counting period chosen.

By virtue of Eq. (12), (14), and (15), either counting distribution can be expressed (at least formally) in terms of the other. Therefore, in the specific cases treated in Sections 4.4, 4.5, and 4.6, both distributions will be computed only when the calculations are perfectly easy.

The mean value of the asynchronous counting distribution can be obtained by differentiation of Eq. (12) and then setting $z = 1$, and is

$$\bar{m} = \tau/\gamma. \tag{16}$$

This is an intuitively sensible result, for it states that, for unit counting period, the asynchronous counting mean is simply the reciprocal of the mean gap. In a space process, it is equal to the traffic density, and in a time process to the traffic volume. Thus the volume density problem of Chapter 3 now appears as a question of relating the asynchronous counting means for the space and time processes.

The mean of the synchronous counting distribution, by Eq. (15) of Section 1.7, can be obtained if we sum Eq. (6) over n, leading to

$$m = \mathscr{L}^{-1} \frac{\phi}{s(1 - \phi)}. \tag{17}$$

4.4 Erlang Process for Headway

As a model for vehicular arrangement, the random process has marked deficiencies. The negative exponential gap distribution declines uniformly from a point $1/\gamma$ on the vertical axis; therefore the probability of a gap between two fixed values increases as these values move towards zero. If the gap under investigation is headway, it is preferable to have the density function pass through the origin, making very small headways increasingly improbable. As we have seen, the Type III distribution is a 'natural' generalization of the negative exponential, and has the required property. Furthermore, by suitable adjustment of the parameters μ and k, the Type III distribution will fit a variety of data.

Therefore, we shall apply the results of Section 4.3 to the Erlang process, defined by

$$\phi(s) = \left(\frac{\mu}{\mu + s}\right)^k \tag{1}$$

from Eq. (3), Section 1.10.

SYNCHRONOUS COUNTING.   Since

$$\frac{\phi^{n+1}}{s} = \left(\frac{\mu}{\mu + s}\right)^{(n+1)k} \frac{1}{s}, \tag{2}$$

and since a factor s^p in the denominator of a Laplace transform merely produces p integrations from 0 to τ, we have

$$P_n(\tau) = 1 - \int_0^\tau \frac{e^{-\mu t}\, \mu^{(n+1)k}\, t^{(n+1)k-1}}{\Gamma[(n+1)k]}\, dt$$

$$= 1 - \frac{\gamma((n+1)k, \mu\tau)}{\Gamma[(n+1)k]}$$

$$= \frac{\Gamma((n+1)k, \mu\tau)}{\Gamma[(n+1)k]} \tag{3}$$

The individual probabilities are

$$p_n(\tau) = \frac{\Gamma[(n+1)k, \mu\tau]}{\Gamma[(n+1)k]} - \frac{\Gamma(nk, \mu\tau)}{\Gamma(nk)}. \tag{4}$$

Abbreviating the Poisson probabilities with parameter $\mu\tau$ by

$$B_n = e^{-\mu\tau}\frac{(\mu\tau)^n}{n!} \tag{5}$$

we have

$$p_n(\tau) = \sum_{j=0}^{(n+1)k-1} B_j - \sum_{j=0}^{nk-1} B_j$$

$$= \sum_{j=nk}^{(n+1)k-1} B_j. \tag{6}$$

Equation (6) states that for synchronous counting of an Erlang process, the probability of observing no cars during time τ is the sum of the first k Poisson terms with parameter $\mu\tau$, the probability of one car is the sum of the next k Poisson terms, and so forth. Thus, theoretical probabilities can be easily found from standard Poisson tables. The generating function for this distribution is

$$\pi(z) = \sum_{n=0}^{\infty} e^{-\mu\tau} z^n \sum_{j=1}^{k} \frac{(\mu\tau)^{nk+j-1}}{(kn+j-1)!}$$

$$= 1 + (z-1) \sum_{j=1}^{\infty} z^{j-1} \frac{\gamma(kj, \mu\tau)}{\Gamma(kj)}. \tag{7}$$

By differentiation of $\pi(z)$, we obtain the pth factorial moments

$$\pi^{(p)}(1) = p \sum_{j=p}^{\infty} (j-1)(j-2) \cdots (j-p+1) A_{jk}, \tag{8}$$

where

$$A_n = \frac{\gamma(n, \mu\tau)}{\Gamma(n)}. \tag{9}$$

For $p = 1$, Eq. (8) can also be obtained by inverting formula (9) of Section 4.3.

The problem of estimation of k and μ from data has not been solved, even for the simplest case of equating theoretical and observed moments, because Eq. (8) have not been solved for k and μ.

ASYNCHRONOUS COUNTING. Substituting into Eq. (12) of Section 4.3, we obtain

$$Q_n(\tau) = \frac{\mu}{k} \left[\int_0^\tau A_{nk}\, dt - \int_0^\tau A_{(n+1)k}\, dt \right]. \tag{10}$$

However, Eq. (10) of Section 1.6 is equivalent to

$$A_{(n+1)k} = A_{nk} - \sum_{j=nk}^{(n+1)k-1} B_j.$$ (11)

Substituting this result into Eq. (10), we find

$$\bar{Q}_n(\tau) = \sum_{j=nk}^{(n+1)k-1} \frac{\mu}{k} \int_0^\tau B_j \, dt,$$ (12)

which, upon integrating, becomes

$$\bar{Q}_n(\tau) = \frac{1}{k} \sum_{j=nk+1}^{(n+1)k} A_j,$$ (13)

or, for individual probabilities

$$\bar{p}_n(\tau) = \frac{1}{k} \sum_{(n-1)k+1}^{nk} A_j - \frac{1}{k} \sum_{nk+1}^{(n+1)k} A_j.$$ (14)

This distribution can also be expressed as weighted sums of Poisson terms:

$$\bar{p}_0(\tau) = \sum_{j=0}^{k-1} \left(1 - \frac{j}{k}\right) B_j$$

$$\bar{p}_n(\tau) = \sum_{j=-k+1}^{k-1} \left(1 - \frac{|j|}{k}\right) B_{nk+j}, \qquad n > 0.$$ (15)

The problem of parameter estimation is somewhat easier for asynchronous counting, since, by Eq. (16) of Section 4.3, we have

$$\bar{m} = \frac{\mu\tau}{k}.$$ (16)

Various other relationships between moments can be found by differentiation of Eq. (17). For example, if $\bar{v}$ is the asynchronous variance,

$$\bar{v} = \frac{2}{k} \int m \, d(\mu\tau) - \frac{\mu^2 \tau^2}{k^2} + \frac{\mu\tau}{k}.$$ (17)

4.5 Translated Distributions for Spacing

If we assume that each car has the same length[†] Δ, there can be no cars spaced nearer each other than Δ, and so the spacing distribution should begin at the point Δ rather than at the origin. Let the gap distribution be

$$g_\Delta(x) = g(x - \Delta), \tag{1}$$

where g is a known gap distribution with counting distribution p_n. What is the counting distribution p_n^Δ corresponding to g_Δ? If the Laplace transforms are respectively ϕ and ϕ_Δ, then

$$\phi_\Delta = e^{-s\Delta} \phi. \tag{2}$$

SYNCHRONOUS COUNTING. The inverse transform required by formula (6) of Section 4.3 can be written

$$\frac{\phi_\Delta^{n+1}}{s} = e^{-s\Delta(n+1)} \left[\phi^{n+1}/s\right]$$

$$= \frac{\phi^{n+1}}{s} \sum_{j=0}^{\infty} \left[-s\Delta(n+1)\right]^j/j!. \tag{3}$$

We know that the inverse transformation of the first factor is simply[‡]

$$Q_n(\tau) = 1 - P_n(\tau). \tag{4}$$

Furthermore, since $Q_n(0) = 0$, the multiplication by powers of s in Eq. (3) has the effect of differentiating the Laplace inverse. Taking the inverse of Eq. (3)

$$Q_n^\Delta = \sum_{j=0}^{\infty} \frac{[-\Delta(n+1)]^j}{j!} \frac{d^j Q_n(\tau)}{d\tau^j}, \tag{5}$$

[†] We will use Δ for a car length, or spacing between consecutive minimum spaced cars (an "augmented car length") throughout the remainder of the book, except in Section 7.7.

[‡] We continue to use τ for the counting period, although a distance is now implied.

or, using Taylor's theorem

$$Q_n^{\Delta}(\tau) = Q_n(\tau - \Delta(n+1)). \tag{6}$$

Before making any hasty applications of formula (6), it will be advisable to examine carefully certain aspects of this distribution. If the counting period is taken to be less than $(n+1)$ car lengths, the τ argument becomes negative, and the formula meaningless. This truncation depends on the value of n taken, and is therefore different for each Q. In fact, since Q_n represents the probability of counting *more than* n cars, beginning *just after* a car occurs, if the counting period is shorter than $n+1$ car lengths, such a count is impossible. Hence, Eq. (6) needs to be augmented to read

$$Q_n^{\Delta}(\tau) = Q_n[\tau - \Delta(n+1)], \qquad \tau > \Delta(n+1)$$
$$Q_n^{\Delta}(\tau) = 0, \qquad \tau \leqslant \Delta(n+1). \tag{7}$$

For commonplace distributions, the individual probabilities p_n can be found by removing the summation sign from the cumulative probabilities P_n, but in the present instance there will be different expressions for P_n for different values of n and range of τ. We must therefore proceed a little more exactly, using the relation

$$p_n = P_n - P_{n-1} = Q_{n-1} - Q_n. \tag{8}$$

As an example, we now take the special case *translated negative exponential*[†]. This means that we assume the spacing between back bumper and following front bumper to be exactly negative exponential. The corresponding counting distribution is Poisson, parameter μ. If we denote the kth Poisson sum with parameter $\mu[\tau - j\Delta]$ by B_k^j, and use Eq. (7) and (8), we obtain successively

$$p_0^{\Delta}(\tau) = \begin{cases} B_1^1, & \tau > \Delta \\ 1, & \tau \leqslant \Delta \end{cases}$$

---

† Because of the lack of aging in a random process, it is the same as *truncated negative exponential*.

$$p_1^\Delta(\tau) = \begin{cases} -B_0{}^1 + B_0{}^2 + B_1{}^2, & \tau > 2\Delta \\ 1 - B_0{}^1, & \Delta < \tau \leqslant 2\Delta \\ 0, & 0 < \tau \leqslant \Delta \end{cases}$$

$$p_2^\Delta(\tau) = \begin{cases} -B_0{}^2 - B_1{}^2 + B_0{}^3 + B_1{}^3 + B_2{}^3, & \tau > 3\Delta \\ 1 - B_0{}^2 - B_1{}^2, & 2\Delta < \tau \leqslant 3\Delta \\ 0, & \Delta < \tau \leqslant 2\Delta \\ 0, & \tau \leqslant \Delta, \end{cases}$$

and in general

$$p_n^\Delta(\tau) = \begin{cases} \sum_{j=0}^{n} B_j{}^{n+1} - \sum_{j=0}^{n-1} B_j{}^n, & \tau > (n+1)\Delta \\ 1 - \sum_{j=0}^{n-1} B_j{}^n, & n\Delta < \tau \leqslant (n+1)\Delta \\ 0, & \tau \leqslant n\Delta, \end{cases} \tag{10}$$

which can also be written

$$p_n^\Delta(\tau) \tag{11}$$

$$= \begin{cases} \dfrac{\Gamma(n+1, \mu[\tau - (n+1)\Delta])}{\Gamma(n+1)} - \dfrac{\Gamma(n, \mu(\tau - n\Delta))}{\Gamma(n),} & \tau > (n+1)\Delta; \\ 1 - \dfrac{\Gamma(n, \mu(\tau - n\Delta))}{\Gamma(n),} & n\Delta < \tau \leqslant (n+1)\Delta, \\ 0, & \tau \leqslant n\Delta. \end{cases}$$

The parallel between this distribution and the asynchronous counting distribution for Erlang headway, Eq. (4) of Section 4.4 is striking. It is also interesting to note that the expression $\mu(\tau - n\Delta)$ can be written

$$\Delta\mu\left(\frac{\tau}{\Delta} - n\right).$$

Here, $\mu\Delta$ is the percentage of road occupied by vehicles, and so corresponds to λ/λ' as used in Chapter 3, and τ/Δ is the counting interval expressed in units of car length.

ASYNCHRONOUS COUNTING. Although a little more complicated, this case does not differ in principle from the synchronous case, and therefore will be treated only briefly. The Laplace transform of $Q_n^\Delta(\tau)$ is

$$\frac{\phi_\Delta{}^n (1 - \phi_\Delta)}{s^2 \gamma} = \frac{e^{-sn\Delta} \phi^n (1 - e^{-s\Delta} \phi)}{s^2 \gamma}. \tag{12}$$

If we try to arrange the right side of Eq. (12) into a product involving the inverse of the asynchronous untranslated tails, the remaining factor is

$$\frac{e^{-sn\Delta} (1 - e^{-s\Delta} \phi)}{1 - \phi}, \tag{13}$$

which is not convenient for Laplace inversion. A better plan is to express the result in terms of the *synchronous* untranslated tails. We can write

$$\frac{\phi_\Delta{}^n (1 - \phi_\Delta)}{s^2 \gamma}$$

$$= \frac{\phi^n}{s} \frac{1}{s\gamma} \sum_{j=0}^{\infty} (-sn\Delta)^j/j! - \frac{\phi^{n+1}}{s} \frac{1}{s\gamma} \sum_{j=0}^{\infty} [-s\Delta(n+1)]^j/j!$$

and, performing operations similar to those for the preceding case, obtain

$$Q_n^\Delta(\tau) = \frac{1}{\gamma} \int_0^{\tau - \Delta n} Q_{n-1}(u)\, du - \frac{1}{\gamma} \int_0^{\tau - \Delta(n+1)} Q_n(u)\, du, \tag{14}$$

where the Q_n are exactly as in the synchronous case. Since these integrals are not usually easy to evaluate explicitly, we leave the result in cumulative form. As in the synchronous case, Eq. (14) will be interpreted differently for the ranges $\tau > (n+1)\Delta$, $n\Delta < \tau \leqslant (n+1)\Delta$ and $\tau \leqslant n\Delta$.

4.6 Compound Gap Distributions

Suppose the cars under consideration can be divided into two categories, Type A and Type B: for example, cars and trucks, leading and following, slow and fast, etc. Let the gap[†] distribution for Type A cars be defined over the interval (a, ∞) with density $g_1(x - a)$ and Laplace transform $e^{-as} \phi_1$ and the corresponding quantities for Type B cars be (b, ∞), $g_2(x - b)$ and $e^{-bs} \phi_2$. If the proportion of Type A cars is p and of Type B cars is $q = 1 - p$, then the whole gap distribution can be written

$$g(x) = p\, g_1(x - a) + q\, g_2(x - b), \tag{1}$$

with Laplace transform

$$\phi(s) = p\, e^{-as}\, \phi_1(s) + q\, e^{-bs}\, \phi_2(s). \tag{2}$$

Therefore the Laplace transform of the tail of the synchronous counting distribution is

$$(1/s)\,[p\, e^{-as}\, \phi_1 + q\, e^{-bs}\, \phi_2]^{n+1} \tag{3}$$

$$= (1/s) \sum_{j=0}^{n+1} \binom{n+1}{j} (p\, e^{-as}\, \phi_1)^j (q\, e^{-bs}\, \phi_2)^{n-j+1}.$$

It is possible, although rather tiresome, to invert formula (3), and express the results in terms of the tails of the untranslated gap components g_1 and g_2. Moreover, our previous experience with the asynchronous case suggests very strongly that the additional factor $(1 - \phi)/s\gamma$ will affect formula (3) only by doubling the number of terms and shifting certain indices. Therefore, instead of pursuing formal manipulations further, we will discuss and apply a particular instance of compound gap theory.

QUEUEING[‡] MODELS FOR TRAFFIC. If the reader will glance back at Chapter 2, he will see that the concept of "distance"

[†] The leading or following gap, depending on interpretation.

[‡] Many authors prefer to speak of *platoons*, *groups*, or *bunches* rather than queues, and there may indeed be a difference between traffic queues and classical queues which is substantial enough to justify the modification. However, since there is no general agreement on what the difference may be, or on definitions of the alternatives, we find it equally convenient to speak of queues.

between queued objects does not occur. The results of queueing theory are therefore consistent with any gap distribution we may care to invoke. Laying aside the time-space question for the moment, we proceed to define several queueing arrangements.

An *Independent Traffic Queueing Model* is constructed as follows: each gap is chosen by performing a Bernoulli experiment with probabilities p and q. If the experiment is a success, the gap is chosen from a gap distribution g_1 and if the experiment is a failure, the gap is chosen from a gap distribution g_2. Cars with g_1 separation are considered to be in the same queue, and cars with g_2 separation are considered to be in separate queues. The most important case of the independent traffic queueing model arises when g_1 represents (in the notation of Section 2.8) D and g_2 represents M. With separation Δ and Poisson parameter λ, we have, by Eq. (1)

$$g(x) = p\,\delta(x - \Delta) + q\,\lambda\,e^{-\lambda(x-\Delta)}, \qquad x \geqslant \Delta. \tag{5}$$

This we shall call an *Independent (D, M) Traffic Queue*. It is equally easy to define an Independent (M, M) queue, but such an arrangement would be intuitively unsound, since queued cars might sometimes be separated by greater distances than unqueued cars. It is important to note that every independent traffic queueing model has geometric probabilities [Eq. (1), Section 1.2] for queues[†] being n cars in length. However, the index is retarded, so that

Prob (queue of n vehicles) $= (1 - p)\,p^{n-1}, \qquad n = 1, 2, \ldots . \tag{6}$

Since independent gaps lead to geometric queue length, we can be sure that any arrangement with other than geometric queue length does not have independent gaps, and therefore does not possess a gap distribution. Such arrangements, nevertheless, do have counting distributions, one of which we will obtain in Section 7.4.

[†] Of course the same thing applies to runs of unqueued, i.e., single, cars, with parameter q instead of p.

An *Efflux Traffic Queueing Model* is constructed by putting the output of an imaginary queue on a moving belt. In this case also, it makes best sense if we choose the imaginary queue to be of the $M/D/1$ type, with parameters λ and Δ. Then the queue length distribution is Borel [Eq. (13), Section 2.6, $r = 1$] and therefore there is no gap distribution. Although the imaginary queue furnishes a convenient way of describing the arrangement, it should not be regarded as a description of the evolution of the traffic.

A *Point Model for Traffic* is one in which cars have no dimension, that is $\Delta = 0$. The independent queueing model and the efflux queueing model may be point models or not, as we wish. The same is not true of the third category of queueing models which we will define in Section 6.5, and which must be a point model.

Consider an independent (D, E_k) traffic queueing model. We have

$$g_1(x) = \delta(x), \qquad g_2(x) = \frac{\mu^k x^{k-1} e^{-\mu x}}{\Gamma(k)},$$

with Laplace transforms

$$\phi_1(s) = 1, \qquad \phi_2(s) = \left(\frac{\mu}{\mu + s}\right)^k. \tag{7}$$

Substituting these values, with $a = b = \Delta$, into Eq. (3), we obtain for the Laplace transform of Q_n in the synchronous case

$$(1/s) \sum_{j=0}^{n+1} e^{-s\Delta(n+1)} \binom{n+1}{j} p^j q^{n-j+1} \left(\frac{\mu}{\mu + s}\right)^{k(n-j+1)} \tag{8}$$

The inverse of the factors involving s is obtained as in previous instances, and is

$$\frac{\mu^r}{\Gamma(r)} \int_{\Delta(n+1)}^{\tau} [t - \Delta(n+1)]^{r-1} e^{-\mu[t - \Delta(n+1)]} dt \tag{9}$$

with $r = k(n - j + 1)$. Formula (9) contains an incomplete gamma function; therefore we can write

$$Q_n^\Delta(\tau) \tag{10}$$

$$= p^{n+1} + \sum_{j=0}^{n} \binom{n+1}{j} p^j q^{n-j+1} \frac{\gamma[k(n-j+1), \mu(\tau - \Delta(n+1))]}{\Gamma[k(n-j+1)]}.$$

When $p = \Delta = 0$, this is equivalent to formula (3) of Section 4.4. When $p = 0$, $k = 1$, it is equivalent to formula (11) of Section 4.5. Various other special cases (and hence queueing models) can be obtained from Eq. (10).

In Chapter 7, we shall return to the problem of moving queues; the queueing models contain sufficiently realistic assumptions to satisfy the requirements laid down in Section 3.1. The point model, previously defined, violates finiteness. Another useful system which violates the finite size of cars is contained in the following model.

Isoveloxic Model for Traffic. In the space-time diagram, each car follows a linear trajectory. Queues cannot form, for cars pass through each other, or equivalently, run on separate tracks. These models are the most remote that we are able to accept as road traffic. However, the space and time counting and gap distributions remain meaningful, and, as we shall see in the next section, the space and time velocity distributions can actually be expressed in terms of one another. An isoveloxic point model is equivalent, in the space-time plane, to a collection of randomly thrown lines.

4.7 Velocity Distributions in Space and Time

The gap and counting distributions contain parameters which enter into the fundamental relationships of Chapter 3; others arise from considerations of velocity. Suppose a finite number of cars are put on a circular track, with each car assigned a particular velocity which it will maintain when unimpeded. This assignment of speeds to the collection will, in the isoveloxic case, constitute a velocity distribution, $f(x)$. A space measurement[†] would give *true*

[†] For example, by an aerial photograph, assuming each car to have a speedometer on its top.

exactly the true velocity distribution; a time measurement[†] would be biased in favor of faster moving cars. We are able to equate the true speed distribution with the space measurement precisely because the road (space) was assumed to be finite, and time infinite. (In the opposite case of an infinite road and finite time period, the road tape would give the correct result. However, it is far more natural to regard an actual road as finite and time as infinite.) The same thing is true if we allow queueing or interference among the cars, although we will defer the analysis of that case to Chapter 7.

As an intermediate distribution between space and time, let $f(x|z)$ be the speed measurement as observed by a car traveling

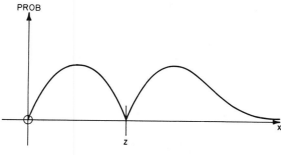

Fig. 11.

freely at constant speed z. Then the time velocity distribution is $f(x|0)$ and the space velocity distribution is $f(x|\infty)$. Note that cars of speed z will never be encountered; therefore the density $f(x|z)$ will consist of two separate parts as shown in Fig. 11. Also, the vehicle is not recording relative velocity $|x - z|$ but the actual absolute velocity of each car it encounters.

In an isoveloxic point model the proportion of cars with speed in the range $(x, x + dx)$ which the test vehicle encounters will depend on the proportion of these cars in the population, and on the rate at which they are being overtaken. This means that we can write

---

[†] For example, by radar at a fixed point.

$$f(x|z) = C|x - z|f(x), \qquad 0 < x < \infty \tag{1}$$

where $f(x)$ is the true speed distribution. The constant C is determined by making

$$\int_0^\infty f(x|z) \, dx = 1,$$

with the result

$$f(x|z) = \frac{|z - x| f(x)}{\int_0^\infty |z - t| f(t) \, dt}. \tag{2}$$

Letting $z \to \infty$, we confirm

$$f(x|\infty) = f(x), \tag{3}$$

and with $z = 0$, we obtain

$$f(x|0) = \frac{x f(x)}{m}, \tag{4}$$

where m is the mean speed. In the future we will use $f(x)$ for the space velocity distribution, and write $\bar{f}(x) = f(x|0)$ for the time velocity distribution. Using $\bar{m}_k$ for the kth central time velocity moment and m_k for the corresponding space moment, we have, directly from Eq. (4)

$$m_k = m \, \bar{m}_{k-1}. \tag{5}$$

Furthermore, dividing Eq. (4) by x and integrating gives

$$m = \text{harmonic mean of time velocity distribution.} \tag{6}$$

This fact resolves the apparent paradox following Eq. (12) of Section 1.7.

Since speed is defined over positive real values, we will sometimes use the Type III distribution for speed distributions. If the time speed distribution is given by Eq. (6) of Section 1.4 with parameters λ and k, then, by Eq. (4) above, the space mean speed has the same distribution with parameters λ and $k - 1$.

It will be noticed that the time velocity distribution given by Eq. (4) stands in the same relation to the true velocity distribution $f(x)$ as does the distribution of a gap surrounding a random point in time to the gap distribution, as shown by Eq. (8) of Section 4.2. This fact is not a coincidence, and can actually be exploited to give an alternative proof of Eq. (4). Suppose we imagine vehicles to be running on a circular track with some assigned true distribution $f(x)$. If they proceed without interference, that is if we consider an isoveloxic model, then the relative frequency of appearance of a given car at some particular point on the track is simply proportional to its speed. We can define the "speed gap" surrounding any point in time as the speed of the next car to appear after that instant. Then, the speed gaps are chosen from the true speeds in just the way that gaps surrounding a point are chosen from true gaps, that is, in proportion to their magnitude. Hence Eq. (8) of Section 4.2 is satisfied, and since the speed gap distribution is only a euphemism for the time speed distribution, Eq. (4) is proven.

4.8 Asymptotic Results

In Sections 4.3 to 4.6 several plausible generalizations of randomness have been exhibited, some of which apply to the time process and others to the space process. If we wish to decide which time arrangements and space arrangements are *true*, a first step might be to discover which ones are *compatible* with each other. A formula analogous to Eq. (4) of Section 4.7, but applying to gaps rather than to speeds, would limit the choice of gap, and hence counting, distributions. Unfortunately, no such result exists at present.

The strongest theorems available are asymptotic in the sense that they show how the arrangement of traffic evolves in remote times or at remote places if an isoveloxic model (with no interference) is postulated. Since it is precisely vehicular interference which suggested the generalizations of randomness, it will not be surprising that when interference is removed, the arrangement will relapse to randomness again.

Let us suppose that every car has zero length and travels in a linear trajectory in the space time plane, as illustrated in Fig. 12. The velocities of cars are to be chosen according to some free speed distribution $f(x)$ quite independently of their positions in the plane.

First, we shall show that if the space arrangement is random at time zero, it is also random at an arbitrary time t. To do this, we need to consider the space arrangement of vehicles within a given

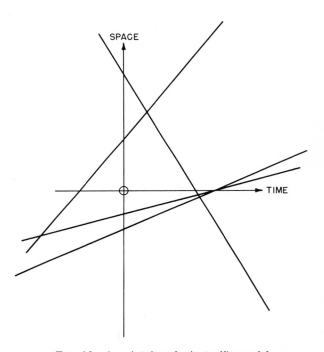

FIG. 12. A point isoveloxic traffic model.

velocity range. Therefore, suppose the domain of the velocity distribution, $(0, \infty)$ to be cut up into smaller subdomains of length Δv. If we consider only vehicles with velocities in one particular range Δv, these vehicles will also be randomly arranged in space at time zero (since initial arrangement and velocities were chosen independently) but with a different parameter. This fact can be understood in the light of the Poisson derivation of Section 1.3:

suppose the cars in various velocity ranges are equated to points of different color dropped randomly on a line. Then the argument leading to the Poisson distribution is valid whether we consider all points of a given color or all points of all colors.

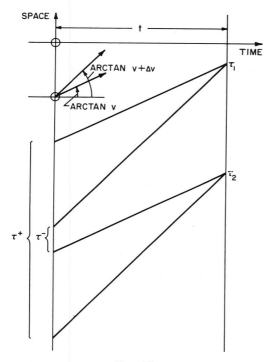

FIG. 13.

Next, choose a counting space of length τ (beginning at τ_2 and ending at $\tau_1 > \tau_2$), at time t, and a particular velocity interval $(v, v + \Delta v)$. Define two new intervals at time zero:

$$\tau^- = [\tau_2 - tv, \tau_1 - t(v + \Delta v)]$$
$$\tau^+ = [\tau_2 - t(v + \Delta v), \tau_1 - tv]. \tag{1}$$

Then, referring to Fig. 13, it is easy to see that every car (in the velocity range) registering in τ must have registered in τ^+ and that every car (in the velocity range) registering in τ^- must register in τ. Therefore, the number of registrations (in the velocity range) in τ is no greater than the number in τ^+ and no less than the number in τ^-. Furthermore, the distribution of number of registrations (of the correct velocity) in τ^- is clearly Poisson with parameter

$$\lambda(\tau - t\Delta v) \int_{v}^{v+\Delta v} f(x)\, dx \qquad (2)$$

since from Eq. (1) the length of τ^- is $\tau - t\, \Delta v$. Similarly, the number of registrations in τ^+ is Poisson with parameter

$$\lambda(\tau + t\, \Delta v) \int_{v}^{v+\Delta v} f(x)\, dx. \qquad (3)$$

Now consider the totality of cars in τ, irrespective of their velocities. Corresponding to each velocity range Δv there will be corresponding intervals τ^- and τ^+ at time zero, and *these will have the same length regardless of which velocity range is chosen*. Of course, the τ^- will not cover the whole line, while the τ^+ will overlap one another; but this fact does not prevent their being perfectly good asynchronous counting spaces for the $t = 0$ axis, because a random arrangement does not distinguish between points on the line.

Since the Laplace transform of the Poisson distribution

$$\phi(s, \lambda) = \sum_{n} e^{-sn} e^{-\lambda} \lambda^n / n! = \exp\left[-\lambda + \lambda e^{-s}\right] \qquad (4)$$

has the property $[\phi(s, \lambda)]^p = \phi(s, p\lambda)$, we know from Section 1.10 that the distribution of sums of Poisson variables is again Poisson with parameter equal to the sum of the separate parameters. Hence, the distribution of points in all the τ^- is Poisson with parameter given by Eq. (2) summed over all the velocity intervals, namely $\lambda(\tau - t\, \Delta v)$; similarly the distribution of points in all the τ^+ is Poisson with parameter $\lambda(\tau + t\, \Delta v)$. The number of registrations in length τ at time t is caught between two Poisson variables, and the mean satisfies

$$\lambda(\tau - t\, \Delta v) \leqslant \text{mean} \leqslant \lambda(\tau + t\, \Delta v). \qquad (5)$$

If we take the limit as $\Delta v \to 0$, we obtain the desired result.

A very similar argument (with a similar conclusion) can be applied to the distribution of points on the horizontal axis, showing that if cars occur at random in space, they also occur at random in time. In this case the Poisson parameter is quite naturally $\lambda \tau m$, where $m = E(v)$.

Next we shall show that randomness is the only arrangement which maintains itself with the passage of time. To do so, we prove an even stronger fact: an arbitrary arrangement in space with continuous velocity distribution approaches randomness as $t \to \infty$.

Consider the space interval (τ_2, τ_1) with $\tau_1 - \tau_2 = \tau$; the number of cars in the interval will be shown to be asymptotically Poisson. Suppose the cars are numbered consecutively at time zero, with x_n and v_n the coordinate and velocity respectively of the nth car. The position of the nth car at time t is therefore $x_n + t v_n$, and it will lie in the interval of length τ if and only if

$$\tau_2 \leqslant x_n + t v_n \leqslant \tau_1. \tag{6}$$

If $N(t)$ denotes the number of cars for which the inequalities (6) hold at time t we wish to prove that

$$\operatorname*{Lim}_{t \to \infty} \text{Prob} \left[N(t) = z \right] = \frac{e^{-\lambda \tau}(\lambda \tau)^z}{z!}, \qquad z = 0, 1, 2, \ldots . \tag{7}$$

This new Poisson result will be obtained with the help of the argument used in Section 1.3 to establish the Poisson distribution as a characteristic of randomness. If the student will look back at that proof, he will see that it began with two segments, of lengths τ and t, where the first lay entirely within the second. When the limit was taken, the segment t increased (as did the number of points) in such a way as to make the density of points approach a constant λ. However, for the argument to be valid, it is not necessary to interpret t as an interval surrounding τ. On the contrary, t might be any extra parameter with the appropriate limiting properties; in the present case we wish it to be elapsed time. We shall therefore state the more general form of the Poisson limit as follows: Given a sequence of Bernoulli trials which depend upon a fixed real number t, so that

$$\text{Prob } (n\text{th trial is a success}) = p_n(t)$$

$$\text{Prob } (n\text{th trial is a failure}) = 1 - p_n(t).$$

If

$$\text{Lim}_{t \to \infty} \sum_{n=1}^{\infty} p_n(t) = \lambda\tau \qquad (8)$$

and

$$\text{Lim}_{t \to \infty} p_n(t) = 0 \qquad \text{for all } n, \qquad (9)$$

then Eq. (7) is satisfied, where $N(t)$ is the total number of successes when the parameter t is used.

The proof is given in Section 1.3. It now remains to show that the isoveloxic traffic model yields probabilities satisfying Eq. (8) and (9). We begin with Eq. (9).

The quantity $p_n(t)$ stands for the probability of inequalities (6) being satisfied, since the infinite sequence of trials is to be equated to the infinite sequence of vehicles. This can be written

$$p_n(t) = \text{Prob}\left[\frac{\tau_2 - x_n}{t} \leqslant v_n \leqslant \frac{\tau_1 - x_n}{t}\right], \qquad (10)$$

or in terms of the velocity distribution $f(x)$,

$$p_n(t) = \int_{(\tau_2 - x_n)/t}^{(\tau_1 - x_n)/t} f(x)\, dx. \qquad (11)$$

Certainly Eq. (9) follows from Eq. (11) if $f(x)$ is continuous. However, it should be noted that if the integral in Eq. (11) is only a mask for a genuine sum of discrete velocity components, then Eq. (9) may not follow. In such a case, the asymptotic distribution might not be Poisson, as is easy to see by imagining all cars to have exactly the same speed. Then any initial arrangement would be perpetuated forever.

If the initial arrangement consists of independently and identically distributed gaps, the condition (8) is proven by Eq. (16)

of Section 4.3. In the more general case of (possibly) dependent gaps, the result is also true, but will not be proven here. The basic idea of the proof is to show that

$$\lim_{t \to \infty} \sum_n p_n(t) = \lambda \tau \int_0^\infty f(x)\, dx = \lambda \tau$$

by breaking down the integral in Eq. (11) into the Riemann sums which define it.

4.9 Renewal Theory

The problems discussed in this chapter constitute a two dimensional (time-space) generalization of the mathematical theory of *renewals*, in which only the time axis is significant. Suppose articles subject to failure, such as light bulbs are replaced or "renewed" by new articles whenever their lifetime comes to an end. The instants of renewal are comparable to the instants of passage of a vehicle, and the gap (say headway) is equivalent to the lifetime of an article. The asynchronous case is called a *general renewal process* and the synchronous case simply a *renewal process*. The starting density is called the *equilibrium delay function*. The principal emphasis in renewal theory has been placed on the counting mean, which, expressed as a function of the counting period τ, is called the *renewal function*. A process corresponding to translated negative exponential gaps is called *quasi-Poisson*.

The renewal functions $\bar{m}(\tau)$ and $m(\tau)$ satisfy a number of relations called *renewal theorems*, of which the simplest is the elementary renewal theorem, exemplified by Eq. (16) of Section 4.3. A more complete statement of the elementary renewal theorem asserts that the reciprocal mean gap is approached by any counting mean (i.e., whether properly asynchronous or not) provided $\tau \to \infty$. Another renewal theorem which is meaningful in traffic theory is Blackwell's Theorem. Suppose we try to find the probability that an arbitrary point on the road will be covered by a car at time t.

If cars are each of length Δ, and of spatial density λ, the answer is clearly $\lambda\Delta$. On the other hand we can argue as follows: let the position of the nth car be x_n, and let the point in question be x. Then

$$\lambda\Delta = \text{Prob } (x \text{ covered})$$

$$= \sum_{n=1}^{\infty} \text{Prob } (x \text{ covered by the } n\text{th car})$$

$$= \sum_{n=1}^{\infty} \text{Prob } (x_n - \Delta \leqslant x \leqslant x_n)$$

$$= \sum_{n=1}^{\infty} \text{Prob } (x \leqslant x_n \leqslant x + \Delta)$$

$$= \sum_{n=1}^{\infty} \int_{x}^{x+\Delta} g^{n*}(z)\, dz$$

$$= \sum_{n=0}^{\infty} [P_n(x) - P_n(x + \Delta)] \qquad \text{[Eq. (3), Section 4.3]}$$

$$= \sum_{n=0}^{\infty} [Q_n(x + \Delta) - Q_n(x)]$$

$$= m(x + \Delta) - m(x). \qquad \text{[Eq. (15), Section 1.7]}. \qquad (1)$$

A generalization of Eq. (1), expressed as a limit for large x and arbitrary counting procedure, is called Blackwell's renewal theorem. We are using the space axis and so would have a separate form of Eq. (1) for each time instant unless the process is in equilibrium.

The traditional approach to the renewal function is by way of integral equations. Suppose we consider the general renewal process (asynchronous counting) and remove the first (incomplete) gap of length z. Then the mean count can be expressed as the mean synchronous count in the remaining period plus the probability that the first gap is of length not exceeding τ. Hence we obtain the integral equation

$$\bar{m}(\tau) = G_0(\tau) + \int_{0}^{\tau} m(\tau - z)\, g_0(z)\, dz. \qquad (2)$$

To remove the bar from the mean, it is clearly sufficient to remove the subscripts from the gap functions. Solutions to integral equations of this type can be found by using Laplace transforms. In fact if we multiply Eq. (2) by $e^{-s\tau}$ and integrate over τ, we find, using Eq. (10) of Section 4.3, Eq. (4) of Section 1.9 and Eq. (17) of Section 4.3, that Eq. (6) of Section 4.2 is confirmed.

In addition to the difference of dimensionality between a renewal process and a traffic process, there is also substantial difference of emphasis. In renewal theory, the counting mean is required for large values of τ; in traffic theory, it is important to have exact counting distributions for finite τ.

4.10 Continuous Traffic

Although we have insisted, both in the postulational system of Chapter 3 and in the present chapter, on the discrete nature of vehicles, it is worthwhile noting that the hydrodynamic analogy mentioned in Chapter 3 comes from treating the counting means as continuous functions of time and space. This kind of simplification is meaningless in renewal theory, because the renewal points have no magnitude in time and no existence in space.

In traffic theory, however, it is certainly sensible to postulate a substance continuously distributed over space at any instant, and having the same counting mean at place x and time t. Thus, we may imagine the functions $\lambda(x, t)$ and $\rho(x, t)$ to arise from the limit $\tau \to 0$, and to satisfy the flow density diagram for given x and t. In this approximation the distinction between synchronous and asynchronous counting disappears. So does the gap distribution, unless one wishes to preserve a fictitious mean gap as the reciprocal of the mean count. It is now possible to postulate various properties of $\lambda(x, t)$ and $\rho(x, t)$ by analogy with known physical substances. For example, one might say first of all that the total traffic substance remains constant, as expressed by the equation

$$\frac{\partial \lambda}{\partial t} + \frac{\partial \rho}{\partial x} = 0. \tag{1}$$

To prove Eq. (1), consider a piece of road R of length Δx and a time interval of length Δt. Let N be the number of cars entering R during Δt and N' be the number leaving. Then

$$N = \rho(x, t)\,\Delta t \qquad \text{and} \qquad N' = \rho(x + \Delta x, t)\,\Delta t$$

approximately, so that we can write

$$\Delta \lambda\, \Delta t = \Delta N = N - N' = [\rho(x, t) - \rho(x + \Delta x, t)]\,\Delta t.$$

Using the first terms of Taylor's series we obtain

$$\Delta \lambda\, \Delta t = -\frac{\partial \rho}{\partial x}\,\Delta x\,\Delta t,$$

from which Eq. (1) follows upon taking the limit as $\Delta x \to 0$.

It would also be necessary to invent postulates to distinguish traffic from classical systems. For example, the quantity of traffic substance at place x at time t must have been at place $x - ut$ at time 0, where u is its velocity. Averaging over u, we obtain the integral equation

$$\lambda(x, t) = \int_0^\infty \lambda(x - ut, 0)\, f(u)\, du \tag{2}$$

for traffic density. If we let $t \to \infty$, we see from Eq. (2) that the density at remote times depends on the density at remote places. If the latter is constant, so is the former; and this fact can be used to construct another proof of decay to randomness.

Equations (1) and (2) are independent of the fundamental diagram (and of each other) in that they do not depend on velocity decreasing with increased density for their validity. This extra fact ($\rho = \lambda v$) might be introduced in a number of ways, such as those given by Eq. (5) and (6) of Section 3.3.

4.11 Dependent Gaps

In every part of this chapter, with the exception of the efflux traffic queueing model and the beginning of Section 4.8, traffic gaps (whether in time or space) were assumed to be independently distributed with the same density function. Each gap, however, is bounded by two cars, or equivalently by two velocities, and there is good reason to believe that a relationship, causal or statistical, may exist between the sizes of the gaps and of the bounding velocities. The car following theories of Section 3.4 assert direct causal connection between the size of a gap and the dynamic variables of its closing car. It is not difficult to imagine that the speed of a car (to say nothing of its acceleration and higher derivatives) will exert some influence on both its gap ahead and its gap behind. For example, when we pass a slow moving car, we feel intuitively that it is safe to move into its lane at once; the implication being that a substantial gap ahead is furnished by slow cars. In the same way, when we are passed by a car traveling at high speed, there is some suggestion that it is followed by a gap of good size. Or, looking at an aerial photograph of a highway, surely one would suppose those cars followed by long gaps and preceded by short ones to be on the average faster moving than those followed by short gaps and preceded by long ones.

If in fact gaps are correlated with both bounding velocities, then successive gaps will be correlated with each other. In such a situation, none of the counting distribution proofs (except asymptotic Poisson counts) employed in this chapter will be valid. However, the basic argument of Eq. (1) and (2) of Section 4.3 is still correct; the failure comes with Eq. (3) and (4). The problem of finding counting distributions therefore reduces, as in the independent cases, to one of obtaining the distribution of sums of variables. But now it will not be sufficient simply to write down a convolution of gap distributions.

Since very little work has been done on this problem, we give only a brief sketch of a formulation. Suppose cars occur at places (taking the space process for convenience) x_0, $x_0 + x_1$, $x_0 + x_1 +$

x_2, ... and suppose the density function for x_0 is $g_0(x)$ and for each succeeding $x_n|x_{n-1}$ is $g(x|y)$. Then the joint distribution of x_0 and x_1 is

$$g(x|y) g_0(y) \qquad (1)$$

and the distribution of x_1 is

$$\int_0^\infty g(x|y) g_0(y) \, dy. \qquad (2)$$

Similarly the distribution of x_2 is

$$\int_0^\infty \int_0^\infty g(x|y) g(y|z) g_0(z) \, dz \, dy \qquad (3)$$

and the distributions of succeeding gaps involve integrals of greater multiplicity.

One very useful fact is that the argument given in Section 1.10 which led to the convolution theorem remains valid as far as Eq. (1). The joint distribution employed there was simply the product of the separate distributions (owing to the assumption of independence) whereas now we need to use, in Eq. (1), a joint distribution such as given by (1) above. We can write the distribution of $z = x_0 + x_1$, therefore, in the form

$$\int_0^\infty \int_0^{z-y} g(x|y) g_0(y) \, dx \, dy. \qquad (4)$$

If we try to continue this approach with even such simple hypotheses as $g_0(x) = \lambda e^{-\lambda x}$, $g(x|y) = y e^{-xy}$, which corresponds in a vague way to the speed-theoretic argument given at the beginning of this section, the calculations soon become intolerable. [cf. Eq. (4) and (5), Section 1.8].

In Section 7.4 we give a very simple model having dependent gaps.

4.12 Comment

The application of the Poisson distribution to traffic problems is the subject of a pamphlet by Gerlough [8] and Schuhl [31]. In this work the reader will find numerical examples, bibliography and a historical summary. The various generalizations of randomness which have been put forward since that time derive mainly from considerations of minimum spacing or dichotomized populations or both.

The translated negative exponential corresponds exactly to what is called in the theory of particle counting a Type I counter, or counter with simple dead time. A car length is equated to the short period during which the counter is unreceptive due to registration. The theory is given very compactly by Feller [6], and the counting distributions by Oliver [20]. Oliver's paper is interesting in that he uses Kolmogoroff type equations (Section 2.3) to obtain counting distributions. He also noticed [21a] that the starting mean implies the Pollaczek formula.

The Erlang gap process is treated by Goodman [10], who obtains the synchronous[†] counting distribution, Eq. (4) of Section 4.4, and calls it the generalized Poisson. This distribution has also been investigated by Whisler [35], Haight [11], and by Haight et al. [12]. The corresponding asynchronous counting distribution appears in Morse's book [19] and Jewell's excellent paper [14]; the latter is also recommended as a general introduction to counting problems for stochastic processes. Whittlesey and Haight [36] give several approximations useful for parameter estimation in both Erlang counting distributions.

The idea of a dichotomized gap population seems to have originated with Schuhl [30], who argues strongly in favor of two negative exponentials, possibly translated. Petigny [24] and Kell [15] also support this hypothesis, although from rather different points of view.

[†] The terms synchronous and asynchronous were suggested to me by Roy Leipnik.

In the special case where one of the exponentials is an impulse, either or both of the counting distributions are called "stuttering Poisson," and are attributed by Jewell [14] to Galliher [7]. Oliver and Thibault [22] treat this case (translated) as applicable to high density traffic. They compute the probability that the count in a fixed time period will be as great as possible, and call this the "probability of maximum pack."

As with car following theories, so with counting distributions: too much emphasis has been placed on theoretical justification and too little on statistical testing. It is probably no exaggeration to say that there is now not one known statistical test specifically designed to compare two counting distributions or two car following theories. The mere ability to fit observed data to hypothetical equations has led some writers into an exaggerated confidence in the truth of the equations. In many such cases the number of parameters free to be chosen is so great as to render the agreement meaningless and the confidence premature.

The results of Section 4.7 seem to be well known, but I do not know who first wrote down Eq. (4). Miller [15] quoted it without attribution in his paper at the 1959 General Motors Symposium, but removed the remark from the printed version [16]. The relation $xf = mg$ between densities f and g is of some theoretical importance, and is mentioned by Breiman [5] (his Proposition 4). More recently it has been studied by Oliver and Jewell [23], and a generalization has been proposed by Haight [13].

The asymptotic approach to randomness is proven under very general conditions by Breiman [2, 3] and (assuming independent gaps) by Miller [16] and Weiss and Herman [34]. The treatment in Section 4.8 is a greatly simplified form of Breiman's results.

It seems very possible that a systematic study of the large literature of renewal theory would suggest useful ideas for traffic analysis. In particular, the problem of independent space and time coordinates should be combined with renewal-theoretic concepts. Smith's paper [33] is a very good introduction to renewal theory, and contains one of the wittiest remarks in mathematical literature.

Continuous traffic models present a difficult problem, for they blend imperceptibly into classical physics. Most of Section 4.10 is derived from Pipes' comments [25] on hydrodynamic models.

There is no doubt that renewal theory or traffic theory with dependent gaps offers new, useful and very challenging problems.[†] The papers of Wold [37] and Domb [5] are mentioned by Smith; Reuschel's paper [26] seems to contain a mixture of car following with dependent gaps. Bartlett's work [7] is unique in that it takes into consideration time-space questions as well as the possibility of gap dependence. By far the most systematic and useful research on this question has been recently carried out by Runnenburg [27, 28, 29]; although it is applied to renewal theory and to queueing theory, it must be possible to mix this judiciously with concepts of random velocity and so obtain truly traffic-theoretic results. We have not, in Section 4.11, gone further than to try to show how one could begin, and what difficulties might be encountered.

REFERENCES

1. Bartlett, M. S., Some Problems Associated with Random Velocities. *Publs. Inst. Statist. L'Université Paris* **6**, No. 4, 261–70 (1957).
2. Breiman, L., "On Some Probability Distributions occurring in Traffic Flow." Presented at the meeting of the International Statistical Institute. Paris France (Summer 1961).
3. Breiman, L., The Poisson Tendency in Traffic Distribution. *Ann. Math. Statist.* (to appear).
4. Breiman, L., Optimal Gambling Systems for Favorable Games. "Fourth Berkeley Symposium on Mathematical Statistics and Probability," Vol. I, pp. 65–78. University of California Press, Berkeley, 1961.
5. Domb, C., The Statistics of Correlated Events. *Phil. Mag.* [7] **41**, 969–82 (1950).
6. Feller, W., On Probability Problems in the Theory of Counters. *In* "Studies and Essays Presented to R. Courant on his 60th Birthday," pp. 105–15. Interscience, New York, 1948.
7. Galliher, H. P., Ordnance Logistics Studies — II: Secondary Item Supply Control. Mass. Inst. Techncl. Interim Technical Report No. 9, Mass. Inst.

[†] This is especially true since very similar problems are appearing in other fields — cf. Gerstein and Kiang [9].

Technol. Project Fundamental Investigations in Methods of Operations Research. Cambridge, Massachusetts, Aug. 1958. (Multilithed.)

8. Gerlough, D. L., The Use of the Poisson Distribution in Highway Traffic. *In* "Poisson and Traffic," pp. 1–58, D. L. Gerlough and A. Schuhl, ENO Foundation, Saugatuck, Connecticut 1955.

9. Gerstein, G. L., and Kiang, N. Y.-S., An Approach to the Quantitative Analysis of Electrophysiological Data from Single Neurons. *Biophys. J.* **1**, No. 1, 15–28 (1960).

10. Goodman, L. A., On the Poisson-Gamma Distribution Problem. *Ann. Inst. Statist. Math.* **3**, 123–25 (1952).

11. Haight, F. A., The Generalized Poisson Distribution. *Ann. Inst. Statist. Math.* **11**, No. 2, 101–5 (1959).

12. Haight, F. A., Whisler, B. F., and Mosher, W. W., Jr., A New Method for Describing the Distribution of Cars on a Road. *Proc. Highway Research Board* **40**, 557–564 (1961).

13. Haight, F. A., A Relationship Between Density Functions. Research Report No. 18. Operations Research Center, Univ. of California, Berkeley California April 30, 1962.

14. Jewell, W. S., The Properties of Recurrent Event Processes. *Operations Research* **8**, No. 4, 446–472 (July-Aug. 1960). Errata **9**, No. 4, 586 (1961).

15. Kell, J. H., A Theory of Traffic Flow on Urban Streets. *Proc. 13th Ann. Western Section Meeting, Inst. Traffic Engrs.* (1960).

16. Miller, A. J., On the Theoretical Justification of the Random Queues Model (unpublished).

17. Miller, A. J., A Queueing Model for the Study of Road Traffic Flow. Presented at the General Motors Symposium on the Theory of Traffic Flow. Warren, Michigan (December, 1959).

18. Miller, A. J., Traffic Flow Treated as a Stochastic Process. *In* Herman, R. (ed.), "Theory of Traffic Flow," pp. 165–74. Proceedings of the Symposium on the Theory of Traffic Flow, held at the General Motors Research Laboratories, Warren, Michigan. Elsevier, Amsterdam, 1961.

19. Morse, P. M., "Queues, Inventories and Maintenance." Wiley, New York, 1958.

20. Oliver, R. M., A Traffic Counting Distribution. Research Report No. 7, Operations Research Center. Univ. of California, Berkeley California, June 23 1961; *Operations Research* **9**, No. 6, 802–810 (Nov.-Dec. 1961).

21. Oliver, R. M., Zero-One Bunching and a Passing Rule. Research Report No. 16, Operations Research Center. Univ. of California, Berkeley California, July 25, 1961.

21a. Oliver, R. M., An elementary derivation of a Pollaczek-Khintchine Formula Research Report 26, operations Research Center, Univ. of California, Berkeley, California.

22. Oliver R. M., and Thibault, B., A High-Flow Traffic Counting Distribution. *Highway Research Board Bull.* No. 356 (1962).

23. Oliver, R. M., and Jewell, W. S. The Distribution of Spread. Research Report No. 20. Operations Research Center, Univ. of California, Berkely California, Dec. 1961.

24. Petigny, B., Le Calcul des Probabilités et la Circulation des Véhicules sur les Chaussées a Deux ou Trois Voies. *Annales des Ponts et Chaussees* **131**, No. 2, 145–223 (March-April 1961).

25. Pipes, L. A., A Comparison of the Lighthill-Whitham and the Richards Theory of Traffic Shock Waves (unpublished).

26. Reuschel, A., Fahrzeugbewegungen in der Kolonne. *Österr. Ingr.-Arch.* **4**, 193–215 (1950).

27. Runnenburg, J. T., On the Use of Markov Processes in One-Server Waiting-Time Problems and Renewal Theory. Thesis, Amsterdam (1960).

28. Runnenburg, J. T., Renewal Theory for Markov-Dependent Random Variables. Mathematisch Centrum Report S 283, Amsterdam, May 1961.

29. Runnenburg, J. T., An Example Illustrating the Possibilities of Renewal Theory and Waiting-Time Theory for Markov-Dependent Arrival Intervals. Mathematisch Centrum Report S 285. Amsterdam May 1961. (Presented at Troisième Congrès International de Téletrafic, Paris, Sept. 11–16, 1961, under title, "On the Use of Markov-Dependent Random Variables in Waiting-Time Theory".)

30. Schuhl, A., Le Calcul des Probabilités et la Circulation des Véhicules sur une Chaussé a Deux Voies. *Annales des Ponts et Chaussées* **125**, 631–63 (1955).

31. Schuhl, A., The Probability Theory Applied to Distribution of Vehicles on Two Lane Highways. *In* "Poisson and Traffic," D. L. Gerlough and A. Schuhl 59–75. ENO Foundation, Saugatuck, Connecticut (1955).

31a. Schuhl, A., Le calcul des probabilités et la répartition des véhicules sur les routes à deux voies de circulation. *Travaux* **39**, no 243, 16–18 (1955).

32. Schuhl, A., Repartition des Espacements de Temps Entre Véhicules Successifs sur une Route a Deux Voies. *Travaux* **39**, No. 249, 633–38 (1955).

33. Smith, W. L., Renewal Theory and its Ramifications. *J. Roy. Statist. Soc.* Ser. B, **20**, 243–302 (1958).

34. Weiss, G., and Herman, R., Statistical Properties of Low-Density Traffic. *Quart. Appl. Math.* **22**, No. 2, 121–130 (July, 1962).

35. Whisler, B. F., A Study of Certain Probability Models Which Aid in Classification of Sequences of Events in Non-Random, Partially Random or Completely Random Categories. M. A. Thesis, American Univ., Washington, D. C., 1960.

36. Whittlesey, J. R. B., and Haight, F. A., Counting Distributions for an Erlang Process. *Ann. Inst. Statist. Math.* **13**, No. 2, 91–103 (1961).

37. Wold, H., On Stationary Point Processes and Markov Chains. *Skandinavisk Aktuarietidskrift* **31**, 229–40 (1948).

CHAPTER 5

The Simple Delay Problem

5.1 Introduction

We now proceed to re-examine the subject matter of Chapter 2 in the traffic context which has been developed in Chapters 3 and 4. The obstacle to free passage in queueing theory was regarded as *service*, and the delay inflicted was consequently called a *service time*. Although these ideas might apply directly to some small area of vehicular traffic theory, such as lubrication or repair, the delay at an intersection is hardly to be regarded as service. The statistical counterpart of this simple fact is that the duration of delays are not necessarily equally distributed random variables, and certainly do not have known density functions. Poisson service in particular appears absurd; a car does not start up at random, but precisely when certain conditions are fulfilled.

We will classify the simple delay problem in various ways, assuming for the most part that the arrival process of the delayed items (on the *side street*) is Poisson. We shall refer to the items delayed as *vehicles* or *pedestrians* according as they do or do not form queues. Pedestrians, however many have accumulated, can all proceed at once when suitable conditions obtain; vehicles must wait their turn. When speaking of pedestrians, we include also a single vehicle, since it will have no delay apart from its own. Results applicable to pedestrians will therefore also apply to vehicles if the side street traffic is sufficiently sparse to permit the queueing effect to be neglected.

Basically, we consider two types of obstacle: an uncontrolled stream of traffic on the *main street*, and a traffic light. Traffic lights can be classified according to their operation, ranging from the fixed cycle of red and green to very elaborate mechanism which respond to the traffic they control.   Main street traffic should be characterized by its gap distribution (including a starting density; the delayed vehicle must arrive independently of main street traffic) and whether or not it is protected by a *stop sign*. A stop sign is assumed to prevent a flying start across the intersection, and hence levels out velocity differences on the side street, leaving only acceleration to distinguish delayed vehicles.

In thinking about the systems outlined above as queues in the sense of Chapter 2, the reader may recognize one further difference. An ordinary service mechanism for a classical queue is assumed to be *responsive*, in the sense that it begins operation whenever there is an arrival to the queue and the previous arrival has finished service. It is precisely because of this property that we were able to assume the waiting time to be zero for arrivals who found the queue empty at their time of arrival.   At a street intersection, however, this is not true.   An arrival may find an empty queue and still have to wait.   The process which permits passage, if it is to be regarded as a service mechanism, is *unresponsive* to the side street arrival, and will permit passage from time to time quite independently of the demand for it.   Taking only one item at a time, an unresponsive mechanism might be thought of as a powered turnstile;   taking several at a time, as a traffic light, and taking randomly distributed numbers at a time, as the main street traffic proposed above.

5.2 Pedestrians Delayed by General Traffic

Suppose a pedestrian arrives at a crossing at time $t = 0$, and requires exactly time T to cross.   Let the time to the arrival of the first vehicle be t_1 with starting density $g_0(x)$, cumulative form $G_0(x)$, and Laplace transform $\phi_0(s)$.   After the first vehicle has passed, let the succeeding headways be $t_2, t_3, \ldots$, each with the density $g(x)$, cumulative form $G(x)$, and Laplace transform $\phi(s)$.

Let $W(x) =$ Prob (pedestrian delay before beginning to cross $\leqslant x$) (1)

have density function $w(x) = W'(x)$ with Laplace transform $\psi(s)$. Whenever $t_1 > T$, there will be no delay; therefore $w(x)$ has a spike at the origin of height

$$\text{Prob}\,(t_1 > T) = 1 - G_0(T) \tag{2}$$

and a continuous component defined over $(0, \infty)$.

Suppose the pedestrian is able to cross for the first time during period t_{n+1}, $n > 0$. Then his delay is

$$\sum_{i=1}^{n} t_i,$$

a simple sum of random variables with known densities. Before applying convolutions directly here, it is necessary to remember that the pedestrian, by hypothesis, has been unable to cross in any of the time periods $t_1, \ldots, t_n$, and therefore each of these must be shorter then T. Hence the density of t_1 is by no means simply $g_0(x)$ as in the unrestricted situation mentioned above, but rather

$$\frac{g_0(x)}{G_0(T)}, \qquad 0 < x < T, \tag{3}$$

where the domain of the starting density has been truncated at the value T. Similarly, the densities of the remaining t_i are just

$$\frac{g(x)}{G(T)}, \qquad 0 < x < T. \tag{4}$$

Hence, the continuous portion of $w(x)$, conditional on the crossing being in the $(n + 1)$ st period is

$$\left(\frac{g_0(x)}{G_0(T)}\right) * \left(\frac{g(x)}{G(T)}\right)^{(n-1)*} \tag{5}$$

and we need only multiply this by the probability of crossing in the $(n + 1)$st period to obtain the unconditional continuous component of $w(x)$. First, however, let us examine the domain of the n-fold convolution given by Formula (5). Since each of the time periods t_i is constrained to the interval $(0, T)$, the sum of n of them must lie in the interval $(0, nT)$. *Therefore the domain of (5) is different for different values of n.*

The probability of crossing in the $(n + 1)$st period is clearly

$$G_0(T)\, G^{n-1}(T)\, [1 - G(T)]. \tag{6}$$

Multiplying (5) and (6), summing on n and taking into consideration the spike at the origin, we have

$$w(x) = [1 - G_0(T)]\, \delta(x) + [1 - G(T)] \sum_{n=1}^{\infty} g_0(x) * g^{(n-1)*}(x) \tag{7}$$

with the convention $g^{0*} = 1$, and bearing in mind the various domains of definition for the convolutions. Taking the Laplace transform in Eq. (7), we obtain

$$\psi(s) = [1 - G_0(T)] + \frac{[1 - G(T)]\, \phi_0(s\,;\, T)}{1 - \phi(s\,;\, T)}, \tag{8}$$

where

$$\phi_0(s\,;\, T) = \int_0^T g_0(x)\, e^{-sx}\, dx \tag{9}$$

and

$$\phi(s\,;\, T) = \int_0^T g(x)\, e^{-sx}\, dx \tag{10}$$

are the "fractional" transforms of g_0 and g respectively, corresponding to the value T. There is no simple relationship between these fractional transforms similar to Eq. (11) of Section 4.2. If we differentiate Eq. (8) and set $s = 0$, we obtain a formula for the mean waiting time:

$$\text{mean wait} = \int_0^T x\, g_0(x)\, dx + \frac{G_0(T)}{1 - G(T)} \int_0^T x\, g(x)\, dx. \tag{11}$$

Equation (7) shows the waiting density in terms of the gap distributions. If we use Eq. (4) of Section 4.3, we can express the cumulative waiting distribution in terms of the asynchronous counting probabilities.   Suppose $(r-1)\ T < x < rT.$ Then

$$W(x) = 1 - G_0(T) + [1 - G(T)] \sum_{n=r}^{\infty} \int_0^x g_0 * g^{(n-1)*} \, dx$$

$$= 1 - G_0(T) + [1 - G(T)] \sum_{n=r}^{\infty} \bar{Q}_{n-1}(x), \qquad (12)$$

$$(r-1)\ T < x < rT.$$

We have seen in Chapter 4 that counting distributions are frequently more tractable mathematically in the synchronous case.   Formula (10) of Section 4.3 enables us to express $W(x)$ in terms of synchronous probabilities:

$$W(x) = 1 - G_0(T) + [1 - G(T)] \frac{1}{\gamma} \int_0^x Q_{r-2}(t) \, dt, \qquad (13)$$

$$(r-1)\ T < x < rT.$$

In Eq. (12) and (13) the piecewise aspect of the delay distribution, which was rather concealed in Eq. (7), is explicitly shown by the letter r.

5.3 Pedestrians Delayed by Random Traffic

Since headways rather than spacings are significant in the crossing problem, it will not be impossible to assume random arrivals.   If we let[†]

$$g_0(x) = g(x) = \mu\, e^{-\mu x}$$
$$G_0(x) = G(x) = 1 - e^{-\mu x}$$
$$\phi_0(s) = \phi(s) = \mu/(\mu + s),$$

[†] μ will represent main road volume throughout this chapter, and λ, side road volume.

then Eq. (8) of Section 5.2 becomes

$$\psi(s) = \frac{(s + \mu) e^{-\mu T}}{s + \mu e^{-(\mu + s)T}}.$$ (1)

This function is not easy to invert. A better procedure is to show that

$$w(x) = e^{-\mu T} \delta(x) + \mu e^{-\mu T} \sum_{j=0}^{r-1} \times$$

$$[-e^{-\mu T}]^j \left\{ \frac{[\mu(x - jT)]^{j-1}}{(j-1)!} + \frac{[\mu(x - jT)]^j}{j!} \right\},$$

$$(r-1)\, T \leqslant x \leqslant rT, \qquad r = 1, 2, \ldots$$ (2)

(where the first term in the braces is taken as zero when $j = 0$) has in fact the Laplace transform (1). This can be done by means of the formula

$$\mathscr{L}(x - b)^n = n!\, s^{-n-1} e^{-sb}, \qquad x > b,$$ (3)

given by Bateman[†].

It is necessary to take care with the various domains of Eq. (2), but the sums of the transformed terms turn out to be simple incomplete geometric series. The mean value of this waiting time distribution can be found directly from Eq. (2), or else by differentiation of Eq. (1), or even from Eq. (11) of Section 4.2, and turns out to be

$$(1/\mu)\, (e^{\mu T} - 1 - \mu T).$$ (4)

If the discrete component is omitted, the mean delay to all delayed pedestrians can be obtained, and is

$$(1/\mu)\, e^{\mu T} - \frac{T}{1 - e^{-\mu T}}.$$ (5)

[†] Erdelyi, A. (ed.), "Tables of Integral Transforms," Vol. 1, p. 137, Eq. (5). McGraw-Hill, New York, 1954. (Bateman Manuscript Project, California Inst. of Tech.)

The variance of the waiting time distribution is

$$(1/\mu^2)\,(e^{2\mu T} - 2\mu T\,e^{\mu T} - 1).\tag{6}$$

5.4 Randomly Arriving Pedestrians

Suppose the instants of pedestrian arrival form a homogeneous Poisson process, parameter λ. Then the results of Section 2.4 apply, regardless of the nature of the traffic process.[†]

In particular the waiting time Laplace transform, Eq. (8), Section 5.2 must satisfy Eq. (8) of Section 2.4, in which ϕ is our present ψ, and

$$\pi(s) = \sum s^n \, \text{Prob}\,(n \text{ pedestrians waiting}).\tag{1}$$

The function $\beta(s)$ was the Laplace transform of the service time distribution; in this case each service period has length zero, since we have not included the crossing time T as part of the delay. Therefore

$$\beta[\lambda(1-s)] = \int_0^\infty e^{-\lambda(1-s)x}\,\delta(x)\,dx = 1$$

and, from Eq. (8) of Section 5.2

$$\pi(s) = [1 - G_0(T)] + \frac{[1 - G(T)]\,\phi_0[\lambda(1-s);\,T]}{1 - \phi[\lambda(1-s);\,T]}\tag{2}$$

is the generating function for pedestrian group size. In the simplest case (random vehicles) this turns out to be a function of the form

$$\frac{A - B\,s}{C - D\,s + P\,e^{Qs}},\tag{3}$$

where the constants are easy to express in terms of the mean values λ and μ and the time to cross T. It is not, however, so easy to

---

[†] As a matter of fact, the arguments of Section 2.4 will be found to be valid for an unresponsive service mechanism, provided the service lag can be added to the service period to produce independent random variables. In the present case, we consider the service time to be zero, and lump the service lag in with the waiting time.

write an explicit formula for the coefficient of s^n in the expansion of (3).

5.5 Blocks and Unblocks

We have seen that the main road traffic acts in some ways like the service mechanism of a queue: it permits passage into or across the road at certain times, which we call *unblocked* moments, and obstructs passage at *blocked* moments. A connected set of blocked (or unblocked) moments forms a blocked (or unblocked) interval, or, briefly, a *block* (or *unblock*).

Let $b(x)$ be the density function for the length of blocks, with Laplace transform $\beta(s)$. First we note that $b(x)$ is defined over $T \leqslant x < \infty$, since every block must be at least as long as T — we may think of each car as pushing a blocked period of length T ahead of it. Let a *diminished block* mean a block with length T removed, so that the distribution of lengths of diminished blocks is defined over $0 \leqslant x < \infty$. If $\gamma(s)$ is the Laplace transform of the length of diminished blocks, then we know from Eq. (2) of Section 4.5 that

$$\beta(s) = e^{-sT} \gamma(s). \tag{1}$$

A diminished block always begins with the passage of a car and ends with the first free passage; therefore it can be considered a waiting time which begins with the passage of a main road car. This means that the distribution of lengths of diminished blocks stands in the same relation to $w(x)$ as synchronous to asynchronous, and that, referring to Eq. (8) of Section 5.2, we can write

$$\gamma(s) = [1 - G(T)] + \frac{[1 - G(T)] \phi(s; T)}{1 - \phi(s; T)} = \frac{1 - G(T)}{1 - \phi(s; T)}. \tag{2}$$

Equations (1) and (2) yield the Laplace transform of the lengths of blocks.

A very similar argument can be used to find the distribution $a(x)$ of lengths of unblocks. Let us define an *augmented unblock* as an unblock with the length T (the T foreshadowed by the car which terminates the unblock, in fact the same T subtracted from the succeeding block to make a diminished block) added. The distribution of lengths of augmented unblocks is simply the distribution of gaps conditional on their exceeding T in length, namely,

$$\frac{g(x)}{1-G(T)}, \qquad T < x < \infty, \tag{3}$$

and therefore

$$a(x) = \frac{g(x+T)}{1-G(T)}, \qquad 0 < x < \infty, \tag{4}$$

with Laplace transform

$$\alpha(s) = \frac{e^{sT}\,\phi(s)}{1-G(T)}. \tag{5}$$

The mean unblock size A, and the mean block size B, are related to each other in a very simple way. From Eq. (1) and (2), we find, upon differentiation, that

$$B = -\beta'(0) = \frac{T[1-G(T)]+\int_0^T x\,g(x)\,dx}{1-G(T)} \tag{6}$$

by virtue of the fact that

$$\phi(0;T) = G(T)$$

and

$$\phi'(0;T) = -\int_0^T x\,g(x)\,dx.$$

Furthermore

$$A = \int_0^\infty x\,a(x)\,dx = \int_0^\infty \frac{x\,g(x+T)}{1-G(T)}\,dx \tag{7}$$

$$= \frac{\gamma - \int_0^T y\,g(y)\,dy - T[1-G(T)]}{1-G(T)}, \tag{8}$$

where, as in Chapter 4, γ is the mean vehicular gap. Equating the integrals from Eq. (6) and (8), we obtain,

$$A + B = \frac{\gamma}{1 - G(T)} = [g_0(T)]^{-1}. \tag{9}$$

If the traffic is random, this formula becomes

$$A + B = (\mu e^{-\mu T})^{-1}. \tag{10}$$

5.6 Delayed Vehicles; General Formulation

Now we turn to the question of queue formation, and recognize this new complication by beginning to refer to the delayed objects as vehicles instead of pedestrians. The *blocks and unblocks* produced by main street traffic quite obviously correspond in a rather strict way to red and green periods of a traffic light, whether that light be *fixed cycle* or *vehicle actuated*. All three of these cases can be studied simultaneously up to the point where it becomes necessary to specify the exact mechanism for the formation of red and green periods.

We therefore consider a queue in which the service mechanism is alternately working and not working, for periods of time α_1, β_1, α_2, β_2, ... Let the input to the queue be random with parameter λ, and suppose that discharge takes place at regular intervals T when the service is working. As a matter of fact, cars do appear to start up from a queue with remarkably even headway, with the exception of the first car, which takes a little longer. However, it is easy to absorb this excess into the red period, so that the term "red period" really refers to slightly more than the exact signal phase. More or less the same pretext can be used to justify ignoring the amber light; depending upon local law and usage, it is treated as either red or green.

In allowing T to stand for the headway between consecutive departures, we intend to suggest a parallel between this quantity and the time required for a pedestrian to cross the road, which has heretofore been called T. The quantity T is in fact a constant service time, and will now be treated as such. Since there was no queueing effect to be considered in the pedestrian crossing problem of Sections 5.2–5.5, we could afford to treat T in a somewhat offhand way.

The unresponsive queue is thus defined, for purposes of road traffic theory, as a queue with alternating periods of working and nonworking service. (It is interesting to notice that the concept can be somewhat generalized. For example, if we require that a person enter a powered revolving turnstile as precisely the beginning of a cubicle, it would certainly be appropriate to say that the service mechanism was almost always inoperative.)

Consider a typical red phase, length β, and let Z be the number of vehicles waiting at the beginning of this period, and X be the number waiting at the end of it. Since there is no service and random arrivals, the distribution of $X - Z$ is

$$\frac{(\lambda\beta)^n e^{-\lambda\beta}}{n!}, \qquad n = 0, 1, 2, \ldots \tag{1}$$

which we will abbreviate $p(n, \lambda\beta)$.

To make a corresponding statement regarding a green period, length α, it is necessary to postulate more precisely the traffic behavior. We will assume that there is regular service and random arrivals until the queue first vanishes, and that after that time traffic moves freely through the intersection without congestion until the beginning of the next red phase. In making such an assumption, we specifically deny the possibility of a new queue building up after the original one disappears, no matter how small a particular headway may be. If T is to be the time for discharge of a vehicle the assumption would be unjustified for headways less than T. We assume, therefore, that T is the time for discharge *only in the case of queued vehicles*; once the original queue is completely discharged, further arrivals during the green period go through the intersection with whatever headway they may have on arrival, even if this is in some cases less than T.

If N is the maximum number of queued vehicles able to clear during the green phase, i.e.,

$$\alpha = NT + \theta T, \qquad 0 \leqslant \theta < 1 \tag{2}$$

we shall refer to N as the number of *slots* provided by the green period. From the queue theoretic point of view, the traffic intensity (during green periods) is defined by

$$\rho = \lambda T \sim \alpha \lambda / N. \tag{3}$$

The probability that exactly n queued items will clear a random arrival, constant service queue beginning with r in the queue before the queue first vanishes is given by the Borel-Tanner probabilities, Eq. (13), Section 2.6, which we abbreviate

$$b(n, r) = A(n, r)\, e^{-\rho n}\, \rho^{n-r}, \qquad n = r, r+1, \ldots, \tag{4}$$

where

$$A(n, r) = \frac{r}{(n-r)!}\, n^{n-r-1}. \tag{5}$$

We do not mention ρ explicitly among the arguments of the Borel-Tanner distribution simply because it will always be understood to have the value given by Eq. (3). The coefficients $A(n, r)$ contain specifically those factors which are independent of ρ.

Let

$$u(x|z) = \text{Prob}\,(X = x | Z = z) \tag{6}$$

and

$$v(z|x) = \text{Prob}\,(Z = z | X = x) \tag{7}$$

be the probabilities respectively of X and Z cars at the beginning of green and red, conditional on their being Z and X at the beginning of the preceding red and green. First we shall compute $v(z|x)$; referring to Fig. 14, we divide the argument into three cases.

Case I. $(x > N)$. The number which will be discharged is precisely N; therefore, in order for z to remain as overflow, $z - x + N$ random arrivals must have occurred. Hence

$$v(z|x) = p(z - x + N, \alpha\lambda), \qquad x > N. \tag{8}$$

Case II. $(z = 0, x \leqslant N)$. The queue must vanish altogether before the green phase ends, and to do so must vanish on one of the values $x, x + 1, \ldots, N$. Since Borel-Tanner probabilities give these individual probabilities, we have

$$v(0|x) = \sum_{j=x}^{N} b(j, x), \qquad x \leqslant N. \tag{9}$$

Case III. $(z > 0, x \leqslant N)$. This case is a little more difficult. The reason for the difficulty may be illustrated by the following fact: particular values of X and Z need not necessarily be associated

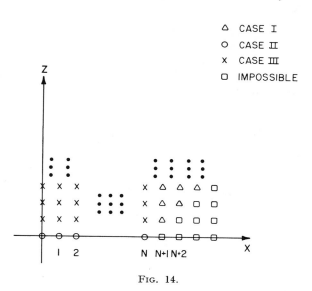

Fig. 14.

with $N - X + Z$ arrivals during the green phase. For, it could happen that first the queue of X would vanish, then the $N - X + Z$ arrivals would pass straight through the intersection, leaving no overflow whatsoever.

Let W denote the number of cars which would pass through the intersection before the queue would first vanish, beginning with X and assuming that the green phase would continue forever. Then the possible associated values of Z and W are set out in the following table:

W	Z
$N + 1$	1
$N + 2$	1 or 2
$N + 3$	1, 2, or 3
$\vdots$	$\vdots$

The Borel-Tanner probabilities have two important connections with W and Z,

$$\text{Prob } (W = w) = b(w, x), \qquad w = x, x + 1, \ldots \qquad (10)$$

by definition, and also

$$\text{Prob } (W = w | Z = z) = b\,(w - N, z), \qquad w \geqslant N + z. \qquad (11)$$

Since, for fixed x, [cf. Eq. (3), Section 1.8]

$$\text{Prob } (Z = z | W = N + z) \, \text{Prob } (W = N + z) = \text{Prob } (Z = z) \qquad (12)$$

$$\text{Prob } (W = N + z | Z = z)$$

we have, using (10) and (11)

$$v(z|x) = e^{\rho z} \, \text{Prob } (Z = z | W = N + z) \, b(N + z, x), \qquad (13)$$

or

$$v(z|x) = e^{\rho z} \, b(N + z, x) \left[1 - \sum_{j=1}^{z-1} \text{Prob } (Z = j | W = N + z) \right]. \qquad (14)$$

The terms in the bracket may be evaluated by using Eq. (12) with z replaced by j.   This gives

$$\text{Prob } (Z = j | W = N + z) \, b(N + z, x) = b(z, j) \, v(j|x). \qquad (15)$$

With these substitutions, we have

$$v(z|x) = e^{\rho z} \left[b(N + z, x) - \sum_{j=1}^{z-1} b(z, j) \, v(j|x) \right] \qquad (16)$$

$$z > 0, \qquad x \leqslant N.$$

Equations (8), (9), and (16) give a recursive process for finding $v(z|x)$ in every case. It will be noted that $v(z|x) = 0$ whenever $x + N < z$, and Fig. 14 shows this to be an impossible transition. The first two values of Eq. (16) are

$$v(1|x) = e^\rho b(N + 1, x)$$

$$v(2|x) = e^{2\rho} [b(N + 2, x) - e^{-\rho} b(N + 1, x)].$$

If we wish to express $v(z|x)$ directly in terms of x, z, N, and ρ, we need only define some new coefficients based upon the Borel-Tanner coefficients of Eq. (5). Let

$$B(z, x) = (-1)^{z+x} \times \tag{17}$$

$$\begin{vmatrix} A(z, z-1) & 1 & 0 & \cdots & 0 \\ A(z, z-2) & A(z-1, z-2) & 1 & \cdots & 0 \\ A(z, z-3) & A(z-1, z-3) & A(z-2, z-3) & \cdots & 0 \\ \vdots & \vdots & \vdots & \vdots & \vdots \\ & & & & 1 \\ A(z, x) & A(z-1, x) & A(z-2, x) & \cdots & A(x+1, x) \end{vmatrix}$$

for $z > x$ and $B(z, z) = 1$. Then

$$v(z|x) = \sum_{j=1}^{z} e^{\rho j} \rho^{z-j} B(z, j) b(N + j, x) \tag{18}$$

$$= e^{-\rho N} \rho^{N+z-x} \sum_{j=1}^{z} B(z, j) A(N + j, x), \quad z > 0, \quad x \leqslant N.$$

The new coefficients $B(z, x)$ can be computed easily from the formula

$$B(z, x) = - \sum_{j=x}^{z-1} A(z, j) B(j, x). \tag{19}$$

The red phase is much simpler; from Eq. (1), we have

$$u(x|z) = p(x - z, \lambda\beta), \quad x = z, z + 1, \ldots \tag{20}$$

The conditional distributions u and v, which are given explicitly by Eq. (8), (9), (18), and (20), can be used to write down the progress of the traffic queue from cycle to cycle, and also the equilibrium queue lengths when the light changes, if such equilibrium exists. First, if we let q_{xy} denote the probability of a transition from x cars at the end of a red period to y cars at the end of the succeeding red period, then

$$q_{xy} = p(y - x + n, (\alpha + \beta)\lambda), \qquad x > N \qquad (21)$$

$$q_{xy} = p(y, \lambda\beta) \sum_{j=x}^{N} b(j, x) + \sum_{i=1}^{y} p(y - i, \lambda\beta) v(i|x), \qquad x \leqslant N.$$

Moreover, if the probabilities

$$\pi_n = \text{Prob } (n \text{ cars waiting at beginning of green } |t = \infty)$$

$$\sigma_n = \text{Prob } (n \text{ cars waiting at beginning of red } |t = \infty)$$

exist, they must satisfy

$$\sigma_n = \sum_{j=0}^{n+N} v(n|j) \pi_j \qquad (22)$$

and

$$\pi_n = \sum_{j=0}^{n} p(n - j, \lambda\beta) \sigma_j. \qquad (23)$$

5.7 Delayed Vehicles; Special Cases

If the traffic control mechanism offers green and red periods of fixed length, so that α and β (and therefore N) are constants, the formulas of Section 5.6 can be applied directly. If, on the other hand, the phase lengths are random variables, these results will need to be modified to allow for this fact. We will give only a few examples of how this can be done, since in the majority of cases the formulas become rather cumbersome. First let us suppose that the traffic control mechanism is precisely the blocks and unblocks of Section 5.5. Then Eq. (8), which depends on the random variable α, would have to be rewritten

$$v(z|x) = \int_0^\infty a(u) \frac{e^{-\lambda u}(\lambda u)^{z-x+N}}{(z-x+N)!} du = \frac{\lambda^{z-x+N}}{(z-x+N)!} \frac{d^{z-x+N} \alpha(\lambda)}{d\lambda^{z-x+N}} \qquad (1)$$

where $a(u)$ and $\alpha(s)$ are given by Eq. (4) and (5) of Section 5.5. The corresponding result, for $x \leqslant N$, is much more difficult, and will not be worked out. It involves providing for the probabilistic nature of N in Eq. (18), Section 5.6. Since N is practically equal to α/T, the distribution over which Eq. (18) must be averaged is essentially the distribution $a(u)$ again. The u distribution is Poisson [Eq. (20), Section 5.6] but must be integrated over the distribution defined by Eqs. (1) and (2) of Section 5.5. Proceeding as above, we can write

$$u(x|z) = \frac{\lambda^{x-z}}{(x-z)!} \frac{d^{x-z} \beta(\lambda)}{d\lambda^{x-z}} \tag{2}$$

where

$$\beta(\lambda) = e^{-\lambda T} \frac{1-G(T)}{1-\phi(\lambda;T)}. \tag{3}$$

Another mechanism for controlling the values of α and β is the vehicle actuated traffic light. These instruments are now being manufactured according to designs far beyond the mathematician's ability to analyze. The illustration which we give here is rather intended to be exemplary; the principles, however, could be used with any particular traffic controller in computer simulation.

We shall assume Poisson traffic on the main street with parameter μ and on the side street with parameter λ. When the main street traffic is given the green light, the green phase will remain for a period A, irrespective of side street traffic. Once time A has expired, the signal will change with the next side street car to arrive. Then the side street will have the green light for a period B, which may be prolonged for an additional period B from the arrival of a car on the side street if a car does arrive during the initial period of length B. The light remains green for the side street until there is a period of length B in which no side street cars arrive; then it changes.

From the point of view of the main stream traffic, each side street car carries a delay of length B with it, once the main street minimum A has elapsed. The distribution of length of main street

red is therefore given by the continuous portion of the distribution
of Eq. (2), Section 5.3 with B replacing T, translated to the interval
(B, ∞). The only difference in derivation is that the delay period
B is now considered to be following the delaying car rather than
preceding it.

The number n of queued cars able to pass through the main
street green period of length α is a random variable defined over
$n = N, N + 1, \ldots$, where N is the number of queued cars able
to pass through during the period A. There will be time for exactly
N queued cars to pass if one side street car arrives in time A, for
exactly $N + 1$ queued cars if no side street car arrives in time A,
but one does during the next time period of length T, and so forth.
Since the probabilities of side street cars arriving in various fixed
time periods are given by the negative exponential tails with
parameter λ, we see at once that

$$\text{Prob}\,(n = N) = 1 - e^{-A\lambda} \tag{4}$$
$$\text{Prob}\,(n = j) = (1 - e^{-\lambda T})\, e^{-\lambda T(j-1)}, \qquad j = N+1, \quad N+2, \ldots .$$

5.8 Delayed Vehicles; Integral Equation Method

It should be clear that direct probability calculations do not
yield very compact expressions for queue length and delay distributions in the vehicular case; in fact the queueing effect seems to
complicate the simple pedestrian delay problem to an extraordinary
degree.   In this section we consider an alternative approach in
which the probabilistic results for each car are made to depend on
those for the preceding car.   We can then assume equilibrium
simply by omitting the car counting subscript.   This method also
leads to equations beyond the possibility of explicit solution, but
it does show a completely new way of treating the problem.   Each
procedure has certain advantages over the other; perhaps a good
workable solution may sometime be found by combining them.

Let the traffic light be red for fixed periods of length β,
beginning with $(0, \beta)$, and green for periods of length α. Then a
time instant t will lie in the kth red phase if and only if

$$k < \frac{t}{\alpha + \beta} < k + \frac{\beta}{\alpha + \beta}, \qquad k = 0, 1, 2, \ldots, \tag{1}$$

which we shall abbreviate $t \in R_k$. Note that the phase count begins with zero rather than unity. Similarly we define $t \in G_k$ to mean

$$k + \frac{\beta}{\alpha + \beta} < \frac{t}{\alpha + \beta} < k + 1, \qquad k = 0, 1, 2, \ldots \tag{2}$$

and $t \in C_k$ to mean

$$k < \frac{t}{\alpha + \beta} < k + 1, \qquad k = 0, 1, 2, \ldots . \tag{3}$$

If there is a k so that $t \in G_k \; (t \in R_k)$ we write $t \in G \; (t \in R)$.

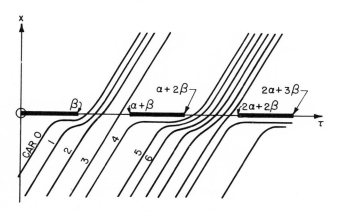

FIG. 15. Natural trajectories.

Suppose the cars travel at a fixed speed v when they are not obstructed by the traffic light or by other cars, as illustrated in Fig. 15, where x represents position and τ true time. It will simplify matters somewhat to replace τ by

$$t = \tau - x/v \tag{4}$$

so that the oblique trajectories are straightened up as in Fig. 16. Since τ and t agree at the traffic light ($x = 0$), inequalities (1), (2), and (3) retain their meaning. We will henceforth adopt the convention of referring to the value of t as "time." In these terms each car has a *fixed* time value before it arrives at the congestion, and another fixed time value after leaving the congestion. For the nth car, $n = 0, 1, 2, \ldots$, we will call these values t_n and $t_n{}'$ and we shall denote the density of $t_n{}'$ conditional on the given value of t_n by $p_n(t_n{}'|t_n)$.

The domain of $t_n{}'$ consists of the value of t_n (in which case the nth car is not delayed), all values between t_n and the next appearance of red, in case $t_n \in G$, and the various discrete instants (separated by

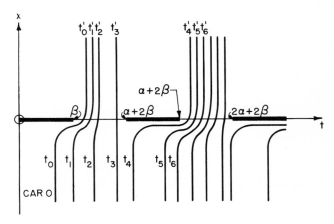

FIG. 16. Modified trajectories.

time T) during succeeding green periods. Let k_n be the cycle in which car n arrives and $k_n{}'$ be the cycle in which car n departs, that is, let $t_n \in C_{k_n}$ and $t_n{}' \in G_{k_n{}'}$. We shall consider the conditional probability distribution in three separate cases: no delay, first to go in green, and other.

Case I: $(t_n{}' = t_n)$. The car is not delayed. This is clearly impossible if $t_n \in R$, so

$$p_n(t_n|t_n) = 0, \qquad t_n \in R. \tag{5}$$

If $t_n \in G$, there will be no delay if $t_{n-1}{}' < t_n - T$. The probability distribution for $t_{n-1}{}'$ is $p_{n-1}(t_{n-1}{}'|t_{n-1})$ or in terms of the gap

$$u_n = t_n - t_{n-1}, \tag{6}$$

$p_{n-1}(t'_{n-1}|t_n - u_n)$. Therefore, for fixed u_n the probability of no delay to the nth car is

$$\sum'_{t'_{n-1} < t_n - T} p_{n-1}(t'_{n-1}|t_n - u_n) \tag{7}$$

and since the density of u_n is $g(u)$, we have

$$p_n(t_n|t_n) = \int_0^\infty g(u) \sum' p_{n-1}(t'_{n-1}|t_n - u)\, du, \qquad t_n \in G. \tag{8}$$

Case II. $(t_n' = (\alpha + \beta)k_n' + T)$. The car is the first to leave during some green period, having been delayed. This can happen in either one of two ways: (i) car n arrives before the beginning of the cycle in which it leaves, and car $(n-1)$ leaves exactly in the last possible position of the preceding green phase, namely

$$t_n < k_n'(\alpha + \beta), \qquad t'_{n-1} = (k_n' - 1)(\alpha + \beta) + NT \tag{9}$$

or else (ii) car n arrives during the red phase of the cycle in which he leaves, and car $(n-1)$ leaves before car n arrives, namely

$$k_n'(\alpha + \beta) < t_n < k_n'(\alpha + \beta) + \beta, \qquad t'_{n-1} < k_n'(\alpha + \beta). \tag{10}$$

Using arguments similar to those employed for Case I, conditions (9) and (10) yield respectively

$$p_n[k_n'(\alpha + \beta) + T|t_n] \tag{11}$$

$$= \int_0^\infty g(u)\, p_{n-1}[(k_n' - 1)(\alpha + \beta) + NT|t_n - u]\, du, \qquad t_n < k_n'(\alpha + \beta)$$

and

$$p_n[k_n'(\alpha + \beta) + T|t_n] \tag{12}$$

$$= \int_0^\infty g(u) \sum' p_{n-1}(t'_{n-1}|t_n - u)\, du, \qquad k_n'(\alpha + \beta) < t_n < k_n'(\alpha + \beta) + \beta$$

where the index of summation is over $t'_{n-1} < k_n'(\alpha + \beta)$. For larger t_n, we have

$$p_n[k_n'(\alpha + \beta) + T|t_n] = 0, \qquad k_n'(\alpha + \beta) + \beta < t_n. \qquad (13)$$

Case III. We know that if car n is delayed by the red light, it must leave at one of the discretely spaced times rT. If on the other hand it is delayed by car $(n - 1)$, then car $(n - 1)$ must be delayed, either by the red light, or by car $(n - 2)$. Pushing this argument back to the preceding red light, we see that some preceding car must leave at one of the discrete times, and so must its successor, delayed by it, and so must all subsequent delayed cars, including finally car n. Therefore we are safe in assuming that car n leaves at time rT after the beginning of some green period, where $r > 1$. Using arguments by now familiar, we obtain

$$p_n[k_n'(\alpha + \beta) + rT|t_n] = \int_0^\infty g(u)\, p_{n-1}[k_n'(\alpha + \beta) + (r-1)T|t_n - u]\, du,$$

$$t_n < k_n'(\alpha + \beta) + rT, \qquad r > 1 \qquad (14)$$

and

$$p_n[k_n'(\alpha + \beta) + rT|t_n] = 0, \qquad t_n > k_n'(\alpha + \beta) + rT, \qquad r > 1. \qquad (15)$$

Next, we shall assume stability, and drop the subscripts. A stable solution should be independent of translations through a cycle; therefore we may also set $k_n' = 0$. Finally, we omit Eqs. (5), (13), and (15) since they are implied by the restricted domains of the other equations. Then Eqs. (8), (11), (12), and (14) yield respectively

$$p(t|t) = \int_0^\infty g(u) \sum_{t' < t - T} p(t'|t - u)\, du, \qquad t \in G \qquad (16)$$

$$p(T|t) = \int_0^\infty g(u)\, p(NT|t - u + \alpha + \beta)\, du, \qquad t < 0 \qquad (17)$$

$$p(T|t) = \int_0^\infty g(u) \sum\nolimits_{t'<0} p(t'|t-u)\, du, \qquad 0 < t < \beta \qquad (18)$$

$$p(rT|t) = \int_0^\infty g(u)\, p\,[(r-1)T|t-u]\, du, \qquad t < rT, \qquad r > 1. \quad (19)$$

5.9 Delayed Vehicles; Bulk Service Model

A *bulk service* queue takes N items through the service mechanism at a time, or all those queueing if there are less than N waiting. With Poisson input (parameter λ) and regular service intervals of length T, the transition matrix for length of queue between consecutive service periods is (cf. Section 2.4)

$$P = \begin{pmatrix} b_0 & b_1 & b_2 & b_3 & b_4 & \cdots \\ b_0 & b_1 & b_2 & b_3 & b_4 & \cdots \\ \vdots & \vdots & \vdots & \vdots & \vdots & \\ b_0 & b_1 & b_2 & b_3 & b_4 & \cdots \\ 0 & b_0 & b_1 & b_2 & b_3 & \cdots \\ 0 & 0 & b_0 & b_1 & b_2 & \cdots \\ \vdots & \vdots & \vdots & \vdots & \vdots & \end{pmatrix} \qquad (1)$$

where b_j is the jth Poisson probability with parameter λT [Eq. (5), Section 4.4] and, the first $N+1$ rows of P are identical. Superficially, it would appear that this queueing model might apply directly to a signalized intersection, for the discharge during the green period indeed resembles bulk service. However, the scheme does not distinguish red and green periods, and consequently does not provide for different treatment of arrivals during those periods. It would be exactly correct if the traffic light discharge took place instantaneously.

For example, we do not wish the transition probability from zero to zero to be equivalent to the probability of zero arrivals during the cycle. We know that traffic lights with sparse traffic can work for long periods of time without overflow (i.e. with a zero to zero transition) and yet pass a steady stream of random traffic. As a matter of fact, it is impossible to say how many cars could be serviced by a traffic light without overflow, since that question is closely connected with speed distributions, driver behavior, etc. In this section we shall make use of the following approximation: *Each car requires time T to get through the light, whether queued or not.* Then the zero to zero transition probability can easily be written

$$b_0 + b_1 + b_2 + \ldots + b_N = B_N.$$

In fact, defining $B_j = \Sigma_{i=0}^{j} b_i$, we need only replace the matrix (1) by

$$\begin{pmatrix} B_N & b_{N+1} & b_{N+2} & b_{N+3} & \cdots \\ B_{N-1} & b_N & b_{N+1} & b_{N+2} & \cdots \\ B_{N-2} & b_{N-1} & b_N & b_{N+1} & \cdots \\ \vdots & \vdots & \vdots & \vdots & \\ b_0(=B_0) & b_1 & b_2 & b_3 & \cdots \\ 0 & b_0 & b_1 & b_2 & \cdots \\ 0 & 0 & b_0 & b_1 & \cdots \\ \vdots & \vdots & \vdots & \vdots & \end{pmatrix} \tag{2}$$

to obtain a queueing model for the signalized intersection which is as valid as the italicized postulate above. Let the equilibrium queue length probabilities be $\sigma_n, n = 0, 1, 2, \ldots$ and let their generating function be $\sigma(s)$. Then, following the argument leading to Eq. (6) of Section 2.4 we see that the asymptotic probabilities satisfy the equations

$$\sigma_0 = B_N \sigma_0 + B_{N-1} \sigma_1 + B_{N-2} \sigma_2 + \ldots + B_0 \sigma_N$$

$$\sigma_1 = b_{N+1} \sigma_0 + b_N \sigma_1 + b_{N-1} \sigma_2 + \ldots + b_1 \sigma_N + b_0 \sigma_{N+1} \tag{3}$$

$$\sigma_2 = b_{N+2} \sigma_0 + b_{N+1} \sigma_1 + b_N \sigma_2 + \ldots + b_2 \sigma_N + b_1 \sigma_{N+1} + b_0 \sigma_{N+2}.$$

If we multiply the nth equation by s^{n+N} and sum, we obtain at once

$$s^N \, \sigma(s) = \sum_{i=0}^{N} \sigma_i \left[B_{N-i} \, s^N + s^i \sum_{j=N-i+1}^{\infty} b_j \, s^j \right] + \tag{4}$$

$$\pi(s) \left[\sum_{j=N+1}^{\infty} \sigma_j \, s^j \right],$$

where $\pi(s)$ is (as in Section 4.3) the generating function of the input traffic. If we define the corresponding partial generating function by

$$\pi_n(s) = \sum_{i=0}^{n} b_j \, s^j \tag{5}$$

so that

$$B_n = \pi_n(1), \tag{6}$$

then Eq. (4) can be written

$$\sigma(s) = \frac{\sum_{i=0}^{N-1} \sigma_i \left[s^N \, \pi_{N-i}(1) - s^i \, \pi_{N-i}(s) \right]}{s^N - \pi(s)}. \tag{7}$$

This determines $\sigma(s)$ from $\pi(s)$ except for the first N coefficients $\sigma_0, \ldots, \sigma_{N-1}$. However $\sigma(s)$ as a power series with positive coefficients must be analytic inside the circle $|s| < 1$, and therefore any zeros of the denominator must also be zeros of the numerator. In the present case $\pi(s) = e^{-\omega + \omega s}$,[†] where $\omega = \lambda(\alpha + \beta)$, since the arrivals are random. By Rouché's theorem

$$s^N - e^{-\omega + \omega s} \tag{8}$$

will have the same number of zeros in and on the unit circle as s^N, namely N. One of these is $s = 1$ and the other $N - 1$, say $s_1, \ldots, s_{N-1}$ must be distinct. For a double zero at the point s would be equivalent to

---

† Note that in this (and the following) section, $\alpha = N$ as a consequence of choosing a natural time scale $T = 1$.

$$s^N = e^{-\lambda + \lambda s}$$

and

$$Ns^{N-1} = \lambda e^{-\lambda + \lambda s}$$
(9)

or

$$1 > s = N/\omega = \rho,$$
(10)

which is the familiar condition for queue instability. Therefore the undetermined coefficients $\sigma_0, \ldots, \sigma_{N-1}$ must satisfy the $N - 1$ equations

$$\sum_{i=0}^{N-1} \sigma_i[s_j^N \pi_{N-i}(1) - s_j^i \pi_{N-i}(s_j)], \qquad j = 1, \ldots, N-1. \quad (11)$$

The set of equations (11) will be augmented by requiring $\sigma(1) = 1$. A single application of L'Hôpital's rule yields

$$\sum_{i=0}^{N-1} \sigma_i[NB_{N-i} - \pi_{N-i}(1) - iB_{N-i}] = N - \omega. \quad (12)$$

But

$$\pi_n'(1) = \omega B_{n-1} \quad (13)$$

and therefore the set of linear equations (11) will be combined with

$$\sum_{i=0}^{N-1} \sigma_i[(N-i)B_{N-i} - \omega B_{N-i-1}] = N - \omega. \quad (14)$$

Finally, we must show that the determinant

$$\begin{vmatrix} NB_N - \omega B_{N-1} & (N-1)B_{N-1} - \omega B_{N-2} & \cdots & B_1 - \omega B_0 \\ s_1^N B_N - \pi_N(s_1) & s_1^N B_{N-1} - s_1 \pi_{N-1}(s_1) & \cdots & s_1^N B_1 - s_1^{N-1} \pi_1(s_1) \\ \vdots & \vdots & & \vdots \\ s_{N-1}^N B_N - \pi_N(s_{N-1}) & s_{N-1}^N B_{N-1} - s_{N-1}\pi_{N-1}(s_{N-1}) & \cdots & s_{N-1}^N B_1 - s_{N-1}^{N-1}\pi_1(s_{N-1}) \end{vmatrix}$$
(15)

does not vanish. If we subtract the ith column from the $(i-1)$st, $i = 2, 3, \ldots, N-1$, we obtain

$$\prod_{j=1}^{N-1}(s_j-1)\begin{vmatrix} \pi_{N-1}(1) & \pi_{N-2}(1) & \cdots & \pi_0(1) \\ \pi_{N-1}(s_1) & \pi_{N-2}(s_1)s_1 & \cdots & \pi_0(s_1)s_1^{N-1} \\ \vdots & \vdots & & \vdots \\ \pi_{N-1}(s_{N-1}) & \pi_{N-2}(s_{N-1})s_{N-1} & \cdots & \pi_0(s_{N-1})s_{N-1}^{N-1} \end{vmatrix}$$

$$(16)$$

which cannot vanish unless two of the s_j are equal to each other, or one of them equal to unity, both of which are untrue.

5.10 Delayed Vehicles; Discrete Time Model

In the preceding section we assumed Poisson traffic on the side street; in the present section we shall assume that it is binomial. The time axis is chopped into equal length intervals, and each interval is characterized as either *red* or *green*, and as containing a car (full) or not (empty). Furthermore,

$$\lambda = \text{Prob (full)} = \text{side street flow rate.} \tag{1}$$

This, as we know from Chapter 1, is the discrete counterpart of the random process — in fact the Poisson counting rule was derived from it. As in the preceding cases, the difficulty lies in formulating the mechanism for the red-green process. In this section we shall work out two possibilities.

First, suppose the red-green process is itself binomial, parameter

$$\mu = \text{Prob (red)} = \text{main street flow rate} \tag{2}$$

assuming that each main street car blocks passage for exactly one time interval. Then, defining σ_i and $\sigma(s)$ as in Section 5.9, we obtain

$$\sigma_0 = \sigma_0(1-\lambda) + \sigma_1(1-\mu)(1-\lambda) \tag{3}$$

$$\sigma_n = \sigma_{n-1}\lambda\mu + \sigma_n\mu(1-\lambda) + \sigma_n\lambda(1-\mu) + \sigma_{n+1}(1-\lambda)(1-\mu),$$

$$n > 0,$$

from probability arguments as in Section 2.3. These equations
lead directly to

$$\sigma(s) = \frac{A s + B}{C s^2 + D s + E} \qquad (4)$$

where

$$A = (1 - \mu - \lambda)(1 - 2\lambda)$$

$$B = (1 - \lambda)(\lambda + \mu - 1)$$

$$C = - \lambda^2 \mu$$

$$D = \lambda (1 + \lambda - \mu - 2\lambda\mu)$$

$$E = - \lambda (1 - \mu)(1 - \lambda).$$

Secondly, let us assume a fixed cycle light. In this case, it is
necessary to modify the formulas of Section 5.9 only by replacing
the Poisson generating function by the binomial generating
function

$$\pi(s) = \sum_{i=0}^{\alpha+\beta} \binom{\alpha + \beta}{i} \lambda^i (1 - \lambda)^{\alpha+\beta-i} s^i = (1 - \lambda + \lambda s)^{\alpha+\beta}, \qquad (5)$$

The first expression which will need to be altered in that section
is (8); the application of Rouché's theorem is still valid, and
Eq. (9) now become

$$s^\alpha = (1 - \lambda + \lambda s)^{\alpha+\beta}$$

$$\alpha s^{\alpha-1} = \lambda(\alpha + \beta)(1 - \lambda + \lambda s)^{\alpha+\beta-1} \qquad (6)$$

which are again equivalent to $\rho > 1$. The elements in the
determinant corresponding to (15) and (16) are partial binomial
sums.

5.11 Comment

The pedestrian crossing problem was first discussed by Adams
[1] in 1937 in connection with an attempt to justify the Poisson
counting distribution for main street traffic. Several mean values

are computed which relate to pedestrian delay, and the agreement of these with their empirical counterparts taken as substantiating the random traffic model from which they were computed. Garwood [13] considers essentially the same problem, although expressed in terms of a single vehicle, and obtains the distribution of Eq. (2), Section 5.3, which is now called Garwood's distribution. Raff [27] defines blocks and shows how the cumulative block distribution is related to the cumulative delay distribution.

The modern approach to the pedestrian problem begins with Tanner's very systematic paper [28], which is coincidently, the last to assume Poisson traffic.[†] Tanner's approach lends itself easily to generalization, and the corresponding formulas for arbitrary main street traffic are given by Mayne [18, 19], although in highly complicated form. Among recent smooth expositions, we mention those of Crowther and Ruid [10], Weiss and Maradudin [29] and Jewell [16]. Our treatment is based on Jewell's.

Oliver [25] gives a very elegant and comprehensive treatment of the block-unblock problem[‡] without reference to the delay question; Section 5.5 is based on this work. The block-unblock process is mathematically equivalent to the dead time process of a Type II particle counter, in which each arriving particle prolongs the dead time by a fixed amount. Feller [12] discusses the mechanism.

Sections 5.6 and 5.7 are based on a paper by Haight [14], and Section 5.8 on a paper by Newell [23]. Newell gives, in addition to the integral equation derivation, some rather intricate special results based on the hypothesis of regular or quasi-random (Type I counter) traffic.

The bulk service approach is due to Bisi [6][‡] and the double discrete (or BMW) model of Section 5.10 to Beckmann et al. [4].

[†] Tanner's work in calling attention to Garwood's distribution was received most enthusiastically by Moskowitz [22], who immediately prepared charts for these probabilities, and applied the results successfully to California data.

[‡] Using the term *gap* to mean what we have called an augmented unblock.

[‡] The ordinary bulk service queue is treated by Bailey [2] in a paper which very much influenced Bisi, Newell [24], and Sections 5.9 and 5.10 above.

The latter paper uses the simple methods exemplified in Section 2.7 to find a relationship between mean delay and mean queue length, and Newell [24] carries out the arguments implied but not given in Section 5.10. Bisi's model is more realistic than the BMW model, and deserves to be more fully worked out. Engel and Meisel [11] give a brief comparison of the two.

There are several variations on the simple delay problem which merit attention, but which will not be treated in Chapter 6. Miller [20] treats delay by a road carrying randomly spaced queues of traffic. Oliver [26] considers an approximation based on the assumption that only one car (at most) will be able to pass through any unblock, as might happen in very dense traffic. Little [17] assumes Poisson traffic, nearly neglects the queueing effect, and obtains mean delay formulas for various turning and merging maneuvers. Beginning with results similar to Adams', Little is able to generalize these for various situations nearby signalized intersections. Weiss and Maradudin [29] replace the constant T by a function $\alpha(t)$ which gives the probability of crossing when a gap of length t is available. This idea reflects not only that different drivers have different crossing requirements, but also that the same driver may become impatient (and hence increasingly intolerant of small t) if required to wait too long. Herman and Weiss [15] and Weiss [30] assume a translated exponential form for the function $\alpha(t)$, and Cohen et al. [9] fit data to a lognormal curve. The latter seems theoretically sound, since many other biological thresholds are known to be lognormal.

Delay theory has been adapted to the study of airport runway delay by Oliver [31].

References

1. Adams, W. F., Road Traffic Considered as a Random Series. *J. Inst. Civil Engrs. London* **4**, 121–30 (1936).
2. Bailey, N. T. J., On Queueing Processes with Bulk Service. *J. Roy. Statist. Soc.* Ser. B, **16**, No. 1, 80–7 (1954).
3. Bartle, R. M., Skoro, V., and Gerlough, D. L., Starting Delay and Time Spacing of Vehicles Entering Signalized Intersections. *Highway Research Board Bull.* **112**, 33–41 (1956).

4. Beckmann, M. J., McGuire, C. B., and Winsten, C. B., "Studies in the Economics of Transportation." Yale Univ. Press, New Haven, Connecticut 1956.

5. Berry, D. S., and Van Til, C. J., A Comparison of Three Methods for Measuring Delay at Intersections. *Traffic Eng.* **25**, 93–99 (Dec. 1954).

6. Bisi, W., Controllo del traffico agli incroci Stradali. *Statistica* **19**, No. 3, 422–33 (1959).

7. Castoldi, L., Alternanza di Code e Regolazione del Traffico in un Incrocio Stradale. *Rend. Seminar. fac. sci. univ. Cagliari* **27** Parts 1 and 2, 48–64 (1957).

8. Castoldi, L., Queue Alternance and Traffic Flow Control at a Crossroad. *Boll. Centro Ricerca Operativa* 5–6 (1958). (English translation of 7 above.)

9. Cohen, J., Dearnaley, E. J., and Hansel, C. E. M., The Risk Taken in Crossing a Road. *Operations Research Quart.* **6**, No. 3, 120–28 (Sept. 1955).

10. Crowther, R. F., and Ruid, D. A., Simple Delays in a Generalized Traffic Flow (unpublished).

11. Engel, E., and Meissl, P., Fahrzeugstau und Wartezeiten an Signalen. *Straße und Autobahnen* **12**, No. 73–76 (Feb. 1961).

12. Feller, W., On Probability Problems in the Theory of Counters. *In* "Studies and Essays Presented to R. Courant on his 60th Birthday," pp. 105–15. Interscience, New York, 1948.

13. Garwood, F., The Application of the Theory of Probability to the Operation of Vehicular Controlled Traffic Signals. *J. Roy. Statist. Soc.* Suppl. **7**, 65–77 (1940).

14. Haight, F. A., Overflow at a Traffic Light. *Biometrika* **46**, Parts 3 and 4, 420–24 (Dec. 1959).

15. Herman, R., and Weiss, G. H., Comments on the Highway Crossing Problem. *Operations Research* **9**, No. 6, 828–840 (Nov.-Dec. 1961).

16. Jewell, W. S., Waiting for a Gap in Traffic. Research Report No. 6, Operations Research Center. Univ. of California, Berkeley California, June 1961.

17. Little, J. D. C., Approximate Expected Delays for Several Maneuvers by a Driver in Poisson Traffic. *Operations Research* **9**, No. 1, 39–52 (Jan.-Feb. 1961).

18. Mayne, A. J., Some Further Results in the Theory of Pedestrians and Road Traffic. *Biometrika* **41**, 375–89 (1954).

19. Mayne, A. J., Corrigenda. *Biometrika* **45**, 291 (1958).

20. Miller, A. J., A Queueing Model for Road Traffic Flow. *J. Roy. Statist. Soc.* Ser. B, **23**, No. 1, 64–90 (1961).

21. Moore, R. L., Pedestrian Choice and Judgement. *Operations Research Quart.* **4**, No. 1, 3–10 (Mar. 1953).

21a. Morgan, J. T., The Unsignalised Intersection in Poisson Traffic (unpublished).

22. Moskowitz, K., Waiting for a Gap in a Traffic Stream. *Proc. Highway Research Board* **33**, 385–95 (1954).

23. Newell, G. F., Statistical Analysis of the Flow of Highway Traffic Through a Signalized Intersection. *Quart. Appl. Math.* **13**, 353–69 (1956).

24. Newell, G. F., Queues for a Fixed-Cycle Traffic Light. *Ann. Math. Statist.* **31**, No. 3, 589–97 (Sept. 1960).

25. Oliver, R. M., Distribution of Gaps and Blocks in a Traffic Stream. Research Report No. 10. Operations Research Center, Univ. of California, Berkeley California, July 25, 1961; *Operations Research* **10**, No. 2, 197–217 (Mar.-Apr., 1962).

26. Oliver, R. M., and Bisbee, E. F., Queueing for Gaps in High Flow Traffic Streams. *Operations Research* **10**, No. 1, 105–114 (Jan.-Feb. 1962).

27. Raff, M. S., The Distribution of Blocks in an Uncongested Stream of Traffic. *J. Am. Statist. Assoc.* **46**, 114–23 (1951).

28. Tanner, J. C., The Delay to Pedestrians Crossing a Road. *Biometrika* **38**, 383–92 (1951).

28a. Tanner, J. C., A Theoretical Analysis of Delays at an Uncontrolled Intersection. (With an appendix by T. R. Sehgal.) Road Research Laboratory. Research Note RN/3937/JCT (1961).

29. Weiss, G. H., and Maradudin, A. A., Some Problems in Traffic Delay. *Operations Research* **10**, No. 1, 74–104 (Jan.-Feb. 1962).

30. Weiss, G. H., On the Pedestrian Queueing Problem. Presented at the 33rd meeting of the International Statistical Institute Paris, 1961.

30a. Weiss, G. H., An Analysis of Pedestrian Queueing (to appear).

31. Oliver, R. M., Airport Runway Capacity and Delays-I. Research Report No. 25, Operations Research Center. Univ. of California, Berkeley, California, August, 1962.

CHAPTER **6** _____

Miscellaneous Problems

6.1 Introduction

In Chapters 4 and 5 we have gone fairly deeply into several questions which appear to be basic to a theory of road traffic, and for which adequate mathematical formulation exists. In the present chapter we will discuss briefly a number of topics which make use of the results previously obtained. In choosing from the great variety of such subjects which have been studied, we take only a few for which the study has been repaid with substantial mathematical results.

6.2 Choice of Traffic Light Phases

In Chapter 5 we treated α and β as fixed constants of a signalized intersection. It is perhaps more practical to regard these quantities as variable, and to use the theory as a means of determining good values for α and β. Suppose we have an intersection in which we distinguish two kinds of traffic, say *horizontal* and *vertical*. Specifically, we take northbound and eastbound traffic to be representative of southbound and westbound traffic respectively, and therefore ignore the latter.

We assume the transition probabilities for each direction to be known in principle from one of the models in Chapter 5. For example q_{xy}, from Eq. (21) of Section 5.6, could be equated to the vertical transitions at the end of consecutive red periods. This expression depends upon

α: Vertical green, horizontal red

β: Horizontal green, vertical red

λ: Vertical input parameter

N: Vertical discharge number.

To simplify matters somewhat, we will take $\theta = 0$ in Eq. (2) of Section 5.6, and measure time in units of T, the time to cross the intersection. This is equivalent to setting $\alpha = N$, so that, omitting λ from the notation, we can write

$$q_{xy} = q_{xy}(\alpha, \beta) \qquad (1)$$

for the vertical probability of transition from x cars at the end of a red period to y cars at the end of the following red period. Note that these are defined at the point of maximum queueing in the whole cycle.

We shall define similar quantities for the horizontal traffic, assuming input parameter μ.[†] Let these be

$$p_{xy} = p_{xy}(\beta, \alpha). \qquad (2)$$

Now, let the cycle length $\alpha + \beta$ be fixed, and let α be determined by the principle: the mean time required for horizontal traffic to form a queue right back to the preceding intersection will be equated to the mean time required for the vertical traffic to form a queue back to its preceding intersection. In fact, if the horizontal block leading up to the light has room for K cars, and the vertical block leading up to the light has room for L cars, and if we define $M(\alpha)$ to be the cycle number during which the vertical queue first equals K and $N(\alpha)$ to be the cycle number during which the horizontal queue first equals L, then we define

$$f(\alpha) = E[M(\alpha)], \qquad g(\alpha) = E[N(\alpha)] \qquad (3)$$

and postulate

$$f(\alpha) = g(\alpha), \qquad (4)$$

from which we wish to determine α.

We shall work with the horizontal process, and first show how the mean number of cycles required to fill up the K places in the

---

[†] If the horizontal input equals the vertical input, it is only necessary to write $q_{xy}(\beta, \alpha)$ for the horizontal transition probabilities.

block can be expressed in terms of the transition probabilities p_{ij}. Let us define

$u_{ij} =$ Prob [horizontal process, starting with i in queue, will have K in queue for the first time during the jth cycle]

so that

$$\sum_{j=1}^{\infty} u_{ij} = 1, \qquad i = 0, 1, \ldots, (K-1), \tag{5}$$

and let the mean value beginning with i in queue be

$$m_i = \sum_{j=1}^{\infty} j \, p_{ij}. \tag{6}$$

It is clear that the u_{ij} can be expressed in terms of the p_{ij} by means of the relationships

$$u_{i,j+1} = \sum_{l=0}^{K-1} u_{lj} \, p_{il}, \qquad j = 1, 2, \ldots \tag{7}$$

and

$$u_{i1} = 1 - \sum_{j=0}^{K-1} p_{ij}. \tag{8}$$

Therefore, we can write

$$m_i = \sum_{j=1}^{\infty} (j+1) \, u_{i,j+1} + u_{i1}$$

$$= \sum_{j=1}^{\infty} \sum_{l=0}^{K-1} j \, u_{lj} \, p_{il} + \sum_{j=1}^{\infty} \sum_{l=0}^{K-1} u_{lj} \, p_{il} + \left(1 - \sum_{j=0}^{K-1} p_{ij}\right),$$

which yields

$$m_i = \sum_{l=0}^{K-1} p_{il} \, m_l + 1, \qquad i = 0, 1, \ldots, K-1. \tag{9}$$

If we let P denote the $K \times K$ matrix (p_{ij}), $i, j = 0, \ldots, (K-1)$, then the set of Eq. (9) can be written

$$(I - P)(m) = (1)$$

where (m) and (1) are the column vectors (m_i) and unity respectively; from this we obtain

$$(m) = (I - P)^{-1}(1), \tag{10}$$

in case $(I - P)$ is nonsingular.

A similar condition will hold for the vertical process. Therefore, in order to apply Eq. (4), it is only necessary to observe initial queue lengths, choose the corresponding rows of the matrices $(I - P)^{-1}$ and $(I - Q)^{-1}$ and set the sum of elements in the rows chosen equal to each other. The resulting equation in α will yield a solution for a signal setting which will be optimal in the sense of Eq. (4). It should be noticed that any such solution will depend upon:

(i)   the model chosen for obtaining p_{ij} and q_{ij},

(ii)   the nonsingularity of $(I - P)$ and $(I - Q)$,

(iii)   the constants λ, μ, K, and L,

(iv)   the initial queue lengths observed.

Condition (iv) could certainly be removed by averaging over the asymptotic queue length distributions.

6.3 Left Turning

In this (and several succeeding) sections, we will use the terminology of right lane driving, which we have so far avoided. In Chapter 7, however, we revert to ambiguous terminology suitable for either system.

Consider an intersection in which the northbound and southbound traffic is always free to move without interference from the horizontal traffic, such as would happen if the horizontal street had stop signs. Suppose there is just one northbound and one southbound lane, and, assuming a discrete time model, let each time slot be of one of the following types: containing

(a)   a car wishing to turn left,

(b)   a car wishing to turn right,

(c)   a car wishing to go straight ahead,

(d)   no car.

The mechanism for turning will be as follows: a car wishing to turn right or go straight ahead can always do so, while a car

wishing to turn left can do so only when the opposing car wishes
to turn left also, or there is no opposing car.   After one such trial
is performed, another takes place with either new cars in both
confronting slots (if both old cars have been able to perform their
desired maneuver) or else just one new car in the confronting slots
(if only one car has been able to perform its desired maneuver).
These rules can be formalized into the following table:

		Northbound			
		Left	Right	Straight	Empty
Southbound	Left	(1,1)	(1,0)	(1,0)	(0,1)
	Right	(0,1)	(1,1)	(1,1)	(0,1)
	Straight	(0,1)	(1,1)	(1,1)	(0,1)
	Empty	(1,0)	(1,0)	(1,0)	(0,0)

where

(1,1) means that both confronting cars are discharged
(1,0) means that only the northbound car is discharged
(0,1) means that only the southbound car is discharged
(0,0) means that no car is discharged.

There are two important things to note about this process.
First, the rows and columns corresponding to *straight* and *right*
are identical; therefore we shall lump these together under the name
not-left. Secondly, the trials are by no means Bernoulli trials, since
whenever a car is held over from one trial to the next one, the
probabilities are altered. Let us assume the following set of probabilities for each time period:

	North	South
Left	λ	λ'
Not-left	μ	μ'
Empty	$1 - \lambda - \mu$	$1 - \lambda' - \mu'$

We have thus three types of trials taking place, depending on whether the northbound, or southbound or neither car is held over. First we shall find the probability of these alternatives. Let

$\pi_1 =$ Prob (Neither car is held over) = Prob (System in state 1)

$\pi_2 =$ Prob (Northbound car held over) = Prob (System in state 2)

$\pi_3 =$ Prob (Southbound car held over) = Prob (System in state 3).

It is clear from (1) and (2) that the process has the transition matrix

$$\begin{pmatrix} 1 - \lambda\mu' - \lambda'\mu & \lambda\mu' & \lambda'\mu \\ 1 - \mu' & \mu' & 0 \\ 1 - \mu & 0 & \mu \end{pmatrix} \tag{3}$$

corresponding to the equilibrium equations

$$\begin{aligned} (-\lambda\mu' - \lambda'\mu)\,\pi_1 + (1-\mu')\,\pi_2 + (1-\mu)\,\pi_3 &= 0 \\ \lambda\mu'\,\pi_1 - (1-\mu')\,\pi_2 \qquad\qquad\quad\ &= 0 \qquad (4) \\ \lambda'\mu\,\pi_1 \qquad\qquad\qquad - (1-\mu)\,\pi_3 &= 0 \end{aligned}$$

which with the normalization conditions yields

$$\begin{aligned} \pi_1 &= (1-\mu)(1-\mu')\Omega \\ \pi_2 &= \lambda\mu'\,(1-\mu)\Omega \qquad (5) \\ \pi_3 &= \lambda'\mu\,(1-\mu')\Omega \end{aligned}$$

where

$$\Omega^{-1} = (1-\mu)(1-\mu') + \lambda\mu'\,(1-\mu) + \lambda'\mu\,(1-\mu').$$

It is not difficult to modify the argument to suit cases in which one of the four probabilities is zero or one.

Next we compute the probability that a northbound car will be discharged, if there is one present. If the system is in state 1, then the northbound car will fail to be discharged only if it wishes left and the southbound car wishes not-left; with the system in state 2, only if the southbound car wishes not-left; while in state 3, the northbound car will be discharged in every case. Therefore

Prob (Northbound car discharged) $= (1 - \lambda\mu')\,\pi_1 + (1-\mu')\,\pi_2 + \pi_3$

$$= (1-\mu')(1 - \mu + \lambda\mu')\Omega. \tag{6}$$

The reciprocal of this quantity is the discharge rate, just as the reciprocal of $(\lambda + \mu)$ is the arrival rate; therefore the traffic intensity for northbound traffic is

$$\rho = (\lambda + \mu)^{-1} (1 - \mu')(1 - \mu + \lambda\mu')\Omega \qquad (7)$$

and the condition for northbound queue stability is

$$(1 - \mu')(1 - \mu + \lambda\mu') > (\lambda + \mu)[(1 - \mu)(1 - \mu') + \qquad (8)$$
$$\lambda\mu'(1 - \mu) + \lambda'\mu(1 - \mu')].$$

If no northbound traffic wishes to turn left, $\lambda = 0$, and the condition (8) reduces to $\mu < 1$, as would be expected. Similarly, if there is no southbound traffic, $\lambda' = \mu' = 0$, and (8) gives the sensible result $\lambda + \mu < 1$.

If southbound traffic is to be stable, the condition (8) has to be replaced by the same expression with primed and unprimed letters exchanged. This leaves Ω fixed, and leads to the following inequalities for both directions to be stable:

$$\Omega^{-1} > \frac{\lambda\mu'(1 - \mu')}{1 - \lambda' - \mu'}$$
$$\qquad (9)$$
$$\Omega^{-1} > \frac{\lambda\mu'(1 - \mu)}{1 - \lambda - \mu}$$

6.4 Multilaned Highways

We shall discuss several problems relating to traffic going in the same direction in r parallel lanes. First we show how multiplicity of lanes affects the gap-counting question. Suppose the traffic in the various lanes proceeds independently, without weaving and merging. Let each individual lane have gap density $g(x)$, starting density $g_0(x)$, with cumulative functions $G(x)$ and $G_0(x)$, with mean value γ. Let the corresponding functions for the whole road be $h(x)$, $h_0(x)$, $H(x)$, and $H_0(x)$. We will show how to express the h functions in terms of the g functions, thereby determining in principle counting distributions, moments, transforms, etc.

At an arbitrary moment in time, the probability that the time to the next car exceeds any fixed value is the joint probability that the time to the next car in each lane exceeds the fixed value. Therefore

$$1 - H_0(x) = [1 - G_0(x)]^r. \tag{1}$$

Substituting from Eq. (1), Section 4.2,

$$\int_x^\infty \frac{1 - H(y)}{\gamma/r} \, dy = \left[\int_x^\infty \frac{1 - G(y)}{\gamma} \, dy \right]^r. \tag{2}$$

Differentiating twice with respect to x, we find $h(x)$:

$$h(x) = [1 - G_0(x)]^{r-2} \left[\frac{(r-1)}{\gamma} [1 - G(x)]^2 + g(x) [1 - G_0(x)] \right]. \tag{3}$$

In the random case, we have $g(x) = (1/\gamma) e^{-x/\gamma}$ from which we obtain

$$h(x) = (r/\gamma) e^{-rx/\gamma}, \tag{4}$$

as would be expected.

The generating function of the pooled counting distribution satisfies Eq. (9) of Section 4.3, and can equally well be expressed in terms of the Laplace transform of $1 - G_0(x)$. Letting

$$\Phi(s) = \mathscr{L}[1 - G_0(x)] \tag{5}$$

we find

$$\Phi(s) = \frac{1 - \phi_0(s)}{s}$$

$$= \frac{\gamma s^2 - 1 + \phi}{\gamma s^2} \tag{6}$$

so that

$$\pi(z) = \mathscr{L}^{-1} \frac{\gamma(1 - s\,\Phi)}{1 - z\gamma s^2\,\Phi - z + z\gamma s}, \tag{7}$$

for the individual lanes. For the whole road, we define

$$\Psi_r(s) = \mathscr{L}[1 - H_0(x)] = \mathscr{L}[1 - G_0(x)]^r \tag{8}$$

and know that the generating function for the counting distribution over the whole road will satisfy an equation like (7), but with Φ replaced by Ψ_r. The relationship between Φ and Ψ_r, and hence the relationship between the lane counting distributions and the total counting distribution is implicit in Eqs. (5) and (8), but not easy to write explicitly. However, transforming the derivative of Eq. (1), we can express recursively:

$$s\,\Psi_r(s) = 1 - r + r\,\frac{1}{2\pi i}\int\limits_{c-i\infty}^{c+i\infty} t\,\Psi_1(t)\,\Psi_{r-1}(s-t)\,dt \qquad (9)$$

Next, consider a road of three lanes in each direction at an intersection. Assume that left turning vehicles must choose the left lane, right turning cars the right lane, but that cars wishing to go straight ahead may choose any of the three lanes. Several of the processes previously discussed are connected with this difficult situation. A car wishing to turn left cannot do so with the freedom implicit in Section 6.2, for it must come to terms with not one but three opposing lanes, one of which contains only forward moving cars and one of which only forward moving or right turning cars. Therefore an additional condition for a successful left turn must be imposed, that all queued cars in the right and center lanes have passed the intersection. The center lane proceeds directly forward without delay (if we assume a queue formed by a traffic light) or else is always empty (if we assume no control). In the right lane, cars wishing to go straight ahead can do so without opposition; cars wishing to turn right should either be subject to some fixed delay, which corresponds to the simple delay of turning, or else to a delay similar to that discussed in Section 5.3, in case they must give way to pedestrians.

When all these conditions are combined, the resulting process is difficult to analyze, although, with the formulas which have been derived so far, it should be amenable to computer simulation. It appears that the crucial relationship, which characterizes the intersection (or the population of drivers using the intersection) is that existing between proportions of straight and turning drivers in the extreme lanes on one hand and asymptotic queue length probabilities in the three lanes on the other.

Finally, we shall mention briefly a generalization of traffic dynamics to two parallel lanes. Suppose the lanes have limiting densities λ_1 and λ_2, but that at time t there is a temporary imbalance characterized by the equation

$$\lambda_1'(t) = -\lambda_2'(t) = C[\lambda_2(t) - \lambda_1(t) - (\lambda_2 - \lambda_1)], \qquad (10)$$

where $\lambda_1(t)$ and $\lambda_2(t)$ are the densities at time t and the primes denote time differentiation. That is, the rate of return to normality is proportional to the difference of deviations from that state. Does there exist a constant α such that Eq. (10) is satisfied by functions of the form

$$\lambda_1(t) = \lambda_1 + a_1 e^{-\alpha t} \qquad (11)$$

$$\lambda_2(t) = \lambda_2 + a_2 e^{-\alpha t}?$$

The combination of Eqs. (10) and (11) yields an expression of the form of Eq. (16) of Section 2.6, for which the solution is given by Eq. (18) of Section 2.6.

It is not difficult to invent equations similar to (10) which might apply to more than two lanes of traffic.

6.5 Sequences of Traffic Controls

In addition to the parallel arrangements discussed in Section 6.4, traffic networks contain many worthwhile analogies with sequences of queues. If a queue is of the simple $M/M/1$ type, it is easy to see that the departing items form a random arrangement. For, if the input parameter is λ and the service parameter μ, then the probability of an empty queue is $1 - \rho$, where $\rho = \lambda/\mu$. Therefore the distance (or time) between departing items is distributed as $\mu e^{-\mu x}$ with probability ρ and as

$$\frac{\lambda\mu}{\mu - \lambda}[e^{-\lambda x} - e^{-\mu x}], \qquad \lambda < \mu \qquad (1)$$

(the distribution of length of a service period plus an arrival period) with probability $(1 - \rho)$. Hence the unconditional distribution of departure gap is

$$\rho\mu e^{-\mu x} + (1 - \rho)\frac{\lambda\mu}{\mu - \lambda}[e^{-\lambda x} - e^{-\mu x}] = \lambda e^{-\lambda x}, \qquad (2)$$

an expression quite independent of the rate of service!

In several of the preceding sections we have seen well enough the disadvantages of an assumption of randomness, but on the other hand, we have also observed many contexts in which randomness is a fairly good approximation. It is not difficult to extend the above result to arbitrary networks of $M/M/p$ queues, although we will not supply the details here.

It is now possible to construct a third type (cf. Section 4.6) of traffic queueing model. A *Random Traffic Queueing Model* is based on the following axioms: (i) zero car length, i.e., it is a point model, (ii) only two types of cars in the system, *slow*, having speed v, and *fast*, having speed infinity, (iii) single car passing from every queue at exponentially distributed intervals. This model, although rather odd in some of its aspects, has, by virtue of Eq. (2) the interesting property of remaining stable over any period of time. The reason why zero car length is required is rather interesting. If the vehicles have finite length, the tail of a queue of vehicles is always advancing and retreating, depending on arrivals and departures; therefore the rate of arrival is not the simple λ given in Eq. (2), but rather biased by the growth and decay at the end of the queue to which vehicles are being attached.

A more realistic situation in which consecutive queues occur is a sequence of signalized intersections. The output from each intersection is very nearly regular; what can be said about the input to the succeeding intersection? This question quite obviously depends on a great many factors, of which the most important is the distance between the intersections. With plenty of time available, we expect traffic to decay to randomness, or at least to a condition not too far removed from randomness. If, on the

other hand, traffic lights are near each other, and very well synchronized, closely packed queues can be perfectly well maintained.

The statistical distribution of a decaying queue is not known
from any postulational system, but in view of the role of the Erlang
model process in previous work, it may safely be assumed that
good empirical approximations would be obtained by assuming the
gap to have a Type III distribution.

Let us consider now a sequence of traffic lights, equally spaced
at distances D, with time $T < \alpha + \beta$ lag between consecutive
lights, where, as in Chapter 5, α is the length of green (now assumed
constant) and β is the length of red (also constant). First, suppose
a car of fixed speed V traverses this system. Its performance is
deterministic, and can be characterized by the number of lights n
between stops, and by k, the number of cycles through which the
nth light has passed before it stops the car. It is easy to see that n
is defined over the positive integers *and infinity* (corresponding to
a car which never has to stop) and k over the positive integers. We
shall say that such a car *is of type* (n, k). If a car is released from
the zeroth light at time zero, it will reach the nth light at time nD/V
if uninterrupted. An arbitrary time t will lie in the kth red period
of light n whenever time $t - nT$ lies in the kth red period of light
zero. Taking inequality (1) of Section 5.8 as referring to the zeroth
light[†] we can say that $t - nT \in R_k$ is equivalent to the point t
lying in the kth red phase of the nth light, and that a car of velocity
V is of type (n, k) whenever

$$k - \frac{\beta}{\alpha + \beta} < \frac{nD/V - nT}{\alpha + \beta} < k, \qquad n = 1, 2, 3, \ldots \qquad (3)$$

and of type ∞ if for some k, $D = VkT$. Defining

$$Z = \frac{D/V - T}{\alpha + \beta} \qquad (4)$$

[†] But with $\beta/(\alpha + \beta)$ subtracted from the extremes to make the process begin
with the start of green rather than red.

the inequalities (3) can be written

$$k - \frac{\beta}{\alpha + \beta} < nZ < k.$$ (5)

Next, we shall assume that V is a random variable with continuous density function $f(v)$. Then the probability that a car is of type ∞ is

$$\pi_\infty = \text{Prob [There is a } k \text{ such that } D = VkT] = 0$$ (6)

and the density function for Z is

$$h(z) = \frac{(\alpha + \beta) D}{[(\alpha + \beta)z + T]^2} f\left[\frac{D}{(\alpha + \beta) z + T}\right].$$ (7)

The probability $\pi_{n,k}$ that a car is of type (n, k) can be found from (5) and (7).

Speed variations which do not change the type of a car will not change its average speed through the system, since any advantage gained (which does not lead to a type change) will be wasted at each waiting point. Therefore the mean speed of a car depends on its type only, and the over-all mean speed afforded by the light system [and speed density $f(x)$] can be written

$$m = \sum_{n, k} \pi_{n, k} \, s_{n, k}$$ (8)

where $s_{n, k}$ is the mean speed of a car of type (n, k). The time of release from the nth light for cars of type (n, k) is the end of the kth red phase; this occurs at time $k(\alpha + \beta) + nT$. Therefore the average speed of a car of type (n, k) is exactly that of a car which managed to get to the point nD in time $k(\alpha + \beta) + nT$. Hence

$$s_{n, k} = \frac{nD}{k(\alpha + \beta) + nT},$$ (9)

and Eqs. (5), (7), and (9) enable us to calculate the mean speed provided by the system in terms of the fixed constants D, T, α, and β. To choose these constants so that m is maximized, we again invoke computing machinery.

6.6 Parking

We begin by considering a parking lot which has places (called *slots*) for exactly N cars. When a car arrives, it occupies a slot if one is available; if not, it joins the queue waiting. The arrival process is Poisson with parameter λ and the duration of parking is negative exponential with parameter μ. Let n be the number parking for $n \leqslant N$ and the number queued for $n > N$. Then the probability of an arrival in time Δt is $\lambda \Delta t + o(\Delta t)$ and the probability of a departure in Δt is $n\mu \Delta t$ when $n \leqslant N$ and $N\mu \Delta t$ when $n > N$. Therefore the differential difference equations for the system are

$$p_0(t + \Delta t) = (1 - \lambda \Delta t)\, p_0(t) + \mu \Delta t(1 - \lambda \Delta t)\, p_1(t)$$

$$p_n(t + \Delta t) = \lambda \Delta t [1 - \mu(n - 1) \Delta t]\, p_{n-1}(t)$$
$$+ (1 - \lambda \Delta t)(1 - n\mu \Delta t)\, p_n(t)$$
$$+ (n + 1)\, \mu \Delta t(1 - \lambda \Delta t)\, p_{n+1}(t), \qquad n \leqslant N$$

$$p_n(t + \Delta t) = \lambda \Delta t [1 - \mu(N - 1)\Delta t]\, p_{n-1}(t)$$
$$+ (1 - \lambda \Delta t)(1 - N\mu \Delta t)\, p_n(t)$$
$$+ N\mu \Delta t(1 - \lambda \Delta t)\, p_{n+1}(t), \qquad n > N$$

$$(1)$$

which lead to the equilibrium equations

$$p_1 - \rho p_0 = 0$$

$$(n + 1)\, p_{n+1} - (\rho + n)\, p_n + \rho p_{n-1} = 0, \qquad n \leqslant N \qquad (2)$$

$$N\, p_{n+1} - (\rho + N)\, p_n + \rho p_{n-1} = 0, \qquad n > N.$$

The solution to these is easily seen to be

$$p_n = \frac{\rho^n}{n!}\, p_0, \qquad\qquad n \leqslant N$$

$$p_n = \frac{\rho^n}{N!\, N^{n-N}}\, p_0, \qquad n > N \qquad\qquad (3)$$

where, using $\Sigma p_n = 1$,

$$p_0 = \frac{N!\,(N-\rho)}{\rho^{N+1} + (N-\rho)\,e^{\rho}\,\Gamma(N+1,\rho)}. \tag{4}$$

Thus, the probabilities for slot occupancy are Poisson–like (with p_0 replacing $e^{-\rho}$) and the queue lengths are geometric. Two special cases are of interest.

INFINITE LOT. Since

$$(e^{\rho}\,p_0)^{-1} = \frac{\Gamma(N+1,\rho)}{\Gamma(N+1)} + \frac{e^{-\rho}\,\rho^{N+1}}{N!\,(N-\rho)}$$

we have

$$\lim_{N \to \infty} p_0 = e^{-\rho} \tag{5}$$

and the occupancy probabilities are genuinely Poisson.

SYSTEM WITH LOSS. If vehicles unable to park go away instead of queueing, we set $p_n = 0$ for $n > N$ and normalization of (3) yields

$$p_n = \frac{\dfrac{\rho^n}{n!}}{\displaystyle\sum_{j=0}^{N}\dfrac{\rho^j}{j!}}, \qquad n = 0, 1, \ldots, N \tag{6}$$

a *truncated Poisson* distribution. In this case the probability that a car cannot park is

$$p_N = \frac{\dfrac{\rho^N}{N!}}{\displaystyle\sum_{j=0}^{N}\dfrac{\rho^j}{j!}}, \tag{7}$$

and the mean number parking is

$$\rho\,\frac{\displaystyle\sum_{j=0}^{N-1}\dfrac{\rho^j}{j!}}{\displaystyle\sum_{j=0}^{N}\dfrac{\rho^j}{j!}}. \tag{8}$$

Equation (7) is called *Erlang's Loss Formula*; in certain applications ρ is determined by experience, p_N by social, economic or political considerations and then N from Erlang's Formula.

From the point of view of a person wishing to park somewhere in a street network, the various curbside slots can be considered as belonging to different lots, depending on their traffic intensity ρ, size N, and *desirability factor* β. For example β^{-1} might measure the distance of the fictitious lot from the drivers destination.

Suppose for $k = 1, 2, \ldots$, lot k has N_k slots, ρ_k traffic intensity and desirability β_k. Since vehicles cannot queue for parking in a street system, we assume each lot operates with loss, so that the probability of finding an empty slot in lot k is, from Eq. (7)

$$\pi_k = \pi_k(\rho_k, N_k) = 1 - \frac{\rho_k^{N_k}/N_k!}{\sum_{j=0}^{N_k} \rho_k^j/j!}. \qquad (9)$$

The driver's problem is then to balance π_k and β_k and so determine the relative advantage in watching lot k.

To obtain specific values for these quantities, let us assume that the driver's destination is at the center of an intersection. Suppose slots are provided on each side of the street with r on each side of a block. Then, ignoring the width of an intersection, there are $8(2k-1)$ slots, $k = 1, 2, 3, \ldots$ equidistant (measured along the street) from the driver's destination. This leads us to define

$$N_k = 8p, \qquad (p-1)r+1 \leqslant k \leqslant pr, \qquad p = 1, 2, \ldots \qquad (10)$$

so that the collection of equidistant slots constitutes a fictitious *lot*. Letting β denote the time (or disadvantage) in walking one slot, we also define

$$\beta_k = \beta k. \qquad (11)$$

We assume that the persons parking form a homogeneous collection with respect to parking time, so that $\mu_k = \mu$, and that the demand for the kth lot is proportional to its size and inversely to its remoteness. This means that the parkers are also homogeneous with respect to destination, and yields

$$\rho_k = \frac{8(2k-1)}{\beta\mu}.$$ (12)

Next we shall make the rather unrealistic assumption that a driver can choose some particular value of k and watch the kth lot. How shall k be chosen? The walking delay from lot k is βk, and the mean delay before parking is not difficult to compute. If lot k is full (probability $1 - \pi_k$), the probability that one particular car will not leave before time t is $e^{-\mu t}$. Therefore the probability that no slot will become available before time t is

$$e^{-\mu t N_k}$$

and the probability that a slot will become available before time t (the cumulative waiting time distribution) is

$$1 - e^{-\mu t N_k}.$$ (13)

The waiting time density for the kth lot is thus

$$\pi_k \, \delta(t) + (1 - \pi_k) \, \mu N_k \, e^{-\mu t N_k},$$ (14)

with mean value

$$\frac{(1 - \pi_k)}{\mu N_k}.$$ (15)

The total expected delay associated with the kth lot is

$$\beta k + \frac{(1 - \pi_k)}{\mu N_k}.$$ (16)

By varying k in formula (16) we can (again appealing to computers) find a most suitable lot if one exists. It may be objected that a driver, assuming he knows the necessary parameters and finds the correct k, cannot drive around the lot he has chosen. As we have defined a lot, it is irregular in shape, disconnected and not accessible without passing through other lots. The driver chooses instead a block to drive around.

However, the average lot number of slots surrounding a block differ by exactly r for contiguous blocks. Hence, if we are content with averages only, a choice of block (i, j) may be regarded as equivalent to the choice of lot $i + j - 1$.

6.7 Merging

A car wishing to merge into high speed traffic is frequently provided with a short *merging lane* which it is supposed to use to accelerate to a speed at which merging with the main flow is more convenient. Mathematically, the position of the driver is rather similar to that of the driver discussed in Chapter 5. If we place a moving coordinate system on the merging car, the main traffic flow past this point is analogous to the flow past a stop sign.

There are, however, two substantial differences. The criterion for safe merging is much more intricate than the criterion for crossing a traffic stream. In addition to a required time before the arrival of the next high speed car (where such an arrival may be ahead or behind the merging car, since it carries the coordinate origin) there is also a space condition to be fulfilled. For example, at very low relative speeds, the merging car could be passed by two cars having arbitrarily long headway as measured by the merging car and yet be separated by a spacing arbitrarily short. The car in Chapter 5 needed only to dart across between its bounding vehicles; the merging car must arrange to occupy space between them.

Furthermore, the merging situation is more general by virtue of the simple fact that the driver who wishes to merge can himself partly control the variables which characterize his position with respect to the traffic flow. If he changes the speed of his own car, he also changes the time (but not the space) criterion for a safe merge, and moreover he can at the same time inspect different parts of the traffic stream for places where these conditions are fulfilled. We have thus a problem of *policy* as well as a purely descriptive problem.

It is important to realize that the two effects of speed variation work against each other. By adjusting his speed to the main stream speed (or mean speed, for a stochastic model) the merging driver achieves the weakest safe merging criteria, but inspects very little (for equal speed model, none) of the stream. With large relative velocity he can look in many parts of the stream but requires much more time for safe merging.

Once we realize that there is a question of policy involved, the merging problem becomes still more difficult to formulate. We need to specify exactly how much information the driver is to be allowed and we also need to set him a very specific goal.

The first requirement is itself more complicated than would appear on the surface. The mere supposition that the merging driver knows the exact equation of motion of every car on the road is not equivalent to perfect information. Does he also know about shock waves, car following, the attentiveness of following drivers, etc.? Is he willing to merge in a situation safe for himself but quickly leading to a rear end collision upstream?

Shall we say that his object is to merge as safely as possible, or as quickly as possible, or as far downstream as possible? In real life, all of these considerations probably play a part in a driver's decisions. For a mathematical model, however, they complicate matters almost beyond any exact formulation.

Next come the descriptive questions: once a driver's information and goals are specified, and his policy obtained, we should be able to recapitulate Chapter 5 and discover the probable effect of this policy and perhaps even a statistical description of the result of many merges choosing individual policies.

It must be obvious from this brief summary that the merging problem is the most difficult encountered so far. Even with the simple go/no-go policy of Chapter 5 the analysis could not be carried to a precise and dogmatic conclusion. In the present case, we can give only a brief discussion of two special cases.

CONSTANT VELOCITIES. If the speed of the merging car is v and of cars in the traffic stream is V, and if the minimum acceptable spacing is S_0, then the required space S can be written

$$S = \max \left[|V - v|T, S_0 \right], \qquad (1)$$

where T is the time required for a safe merge. If $W(x)$ is defined for this traffic stream by Eq. (13) of Section 5.2, where T retains its present meaning, we have no difficulty in expressing

$$V(x) = \text{Prob [Initial distance to (gap} \geqslant S) \text{ is } \leqslant x]} \qquad (2)$$

in terms of $W(x)$. For

$$V(x) = \text{Prob [Time to (gap} \geqslant S/V) \text{ is } \leqslant x/V]}$$
$$= W(x/V), \qquad (3)$$

where S/V is used in place of T.

If $U(x)$ is the cumulative form of the distribution of distance which the merging vehicle must travel before a safe merge is possible, then

$$U(x) = W\left[\frac{|V - v|x}{Vv}\right]. \qquad (4)$$

VARIABLE VELOCITY. Suppose v can be changed by the merging driver, at least within a certain range. What policy shall we adopt? We now need to make the merging lane finite in length, otherwise policies such as "never merge" would have to be allowed. Suppose the lane length is L. At the same time we must prevent the merger from adopting arbitrarily slow speeds and thereby artificially prolonging L. Hence we set v_0, his speed at entry as the least value v can have. Let v_m be the highest speed he can obtain in length L. For example, with exponential acceleration we might postulate

$$v = v_m - (v_m - v_0)\, e^{-\beta t} \qquad (5)$$

as the maximum speed at time t, where β is a constant for a single driver.

Let x be the driver's position in the acceleration lane, $0 \leqslant x \leqslant L$ and y his position relative to the (constant speed V) traffic stream. We will take $y = 0$ and $t = 0$ at the place and time where the car first enters the merging lane and suppose y to be measured positively downstream (where the merging driver improves his position) and negatively upstream.

Let t_L be the least time required to use up the lane L; for example the value of t obtained by integrating Eq. (5) with respect to t and setting $x = L$. Then the best possible merging result, y_{max} is defined by

$$y_{max} = t_L(v - V). \qquad (6)$$

When the merging car arrives, let the distance from L back to the first vehicle in the traffic stream be d_1, from that car back to the next be d_2, and so forth. If the merging vehicle is barely going to fit into the first gap, its nose must arrive at $x = L$ exactly when the gap has shrunk to length Δ, a car length. This uses time t_L, during which the stream has traveled Vt_L. Therefore,

$$L - d_1 + t_L V = L - \Delta \tag{7}$$

or

$$d_1 = \Delta + t_L V \tag{8}$$

for the barely possible merge into the first gap. Defining

$$C = \Delta + t_L V, \tag{9}$$

merging into d_1 is possible when $d_1 \geqslant C$ and impossible otherwise. If the distribution of gaps is negative exponential, the probability of a merge into d_1 is

$$P_1 = \int_C^\infty \lambda e^{-\lambda x} dx = e^{-\lambda C}, \tag{10}$$

where λ is the traffic stream density.

The probability that d_1 will be unsatisfactory but d_2 satisfactory, is the probability that

$$d_1 < C, \qquad d_1 + d_2 \geqslant C, \qquad d_2 \geqslant \Delta. \tag{11}$$

Hence, for Poisson traffic

$$P_2 = \int_C^\infty \int_0^C \lambda^2 e^{-\lambda(x+y)} dx\, dy + \int_\Delta^C \int_{C-y}^C \lambda^2 e^{-\lambda(x+y)} dx\, dy$$

$$= e^{-\lambda C} [1 - e^{-\gamma\Delta} + \lambda(C - \Delta)]. \tag{12}$$

It is easy to obtain successive equations. For example, the third stage uses the inequalities

$$d_1 + d_2 < C, \qquad d_1 + d_2 + d_3 \geqslant C, \qquad d_3 \geqslant \Delta \tag{13}$$

which can be reduced to

$$x < C, \qquad x + y \geqslant C, \qquad y \geqslant \Delta, \tag{14}$$

where $x = d_1 + d_2$ and $y = d_3$. In this way, we find that the probability of fitting into the nth slot is given by the formula

$$P_n = \int\limits_C^\infty \int\limits_0^C \lambda e^{-\lambda y} \frac{\lambda^{n-1} x^{n-2}}{(n-2)!} e^{-\lambda x} \, dx \, dy + \tag{15}$$

$$\int\limits_\Delta^C \int\limits_{C-y}^C \lambda e^{-\lambda y} \frac{\lambda^{n-1} x^{n-2}}{(n-2)!} e^{-\lambda x} \, dx \, dy.$$

6.8 Bottleneck

Consider a north-south road which contains a section permitting only one way traffic. Northbound traffic will use this section until the section becomes empty for the first time, and then queued southbound cars, if any, take over. When there is not a demand from either side, the road remains empty until the first car arrives from either direction. Thus the history of the section can be divided into periods during which it is dominated by northbound, dominated by southbound, and empty. Let the northbound input be Poisson with parameter λ and the southbound input be Poisson with parameter μ. There is no loss in generality, and some gain in simplicity, in assuming all cars take unit time to traverse the section. Hence, if a northbound period begins with r cars queued, the probability that exactly n cars will pass through before the northbound dominance ends is equal to the duration of northbound dominance, and is given by Eq. (13) of Section 2.6. On the other hand, if the period of northbound dominance is given, the distribution of number queueing at the end of the period is a simple Poisson quantity. Thus the Poisson distribution and Borel-Tanner distribution are complimentary conditional distributions for this process just as in Section 5.6. In fact, the traffic bottleneck can be considered equally well to be an intersection, but governed by neither traffic light nor stop sign (establishing main and secondary roads). The only difference lies in the symmetry existing when the road is empty. With a traffic light no car is permitted to go against the red, even if there is no opposition; with a stop sign a minor road car cannot establish dominance even if he arrives before (but time $< T$ before) a main road car. In the present case there are no such restrictions.

Let the probabilities of northbound dominance, southbound dominance and emptiness be respectively[†] π_1, π_2, and π_0. Let the densities of durations of the three types be f, g, and h (in the order listed above) and the Laplace transforms be ϕ, ψ, and χ. It is easy to see at once that

$$h(x) = (\lambda + \mu)\, e^{-(\lambda+\mu)x}, \qquad \chi(t) = \frac{\lambda + \mu}{\lambda + \mu + t}, \qquad (1)$$

since an empty period is terminated by an arrival from either of the Poisson streams. Letting p_{ij} denote the probability of a transition from an arbitrarily chosen state i to a state j, where $i, j = 0, 1, 2$ denote the same thing as for the π_i, we easily find

$$P = (p_{ij}) = \begin{pmatrix} 0 & \dfrac{\lambda}{\lambda+\mu} & \dfrac{\mu}{\lambda+\mu} \\ \phi(\mu) & 0 & 1 - \phi(\mu) \\ \psi(\lambda) & 1 - \psi(\lambda) & 0 \end{pmatrix} \qquad (2)$$

If q_{ij} is the corresponding probability of a transition from state i to an arbitrarily chosen state j, then p_{ij}, q_{ij}, and π_i satisfy

$$\pi_0 = p_{10}\,\pi_1 + p_{20}\,\pi_2 = q_{01}\,\pi_1 + q_{02}\,\pi_2$$
$$\pi_1 = p_{21}\,\pi_2 + p_{01}\,\pi_0 = q_{12}\,\pi_2 + q_{10}\,\pi_0 \qquad (3)$$
$$\pi_2 = p_{02}\,\pi_0 + p_{12}\,\pi_1 = q_{20}\,\pi_0 + q_{21}\,\pi_1.$$

[†] These are not the probabilities that an arbitrary point lies in a period of the three types; cf. the discussion of Eq. (4), Section 4.7.

Using the abbreviations

$$\phi(\mu) = \phi, \qquad \psi(\lambda) = \psi, \qquad \gamma = \phi + \psi - \phi\psi$$

$$\delta_1 = \lambda + \mu - \lambda\phi, \qquad \delta_2 = \lambda + \mu - \mu\psi \tag{4}$$

we easily express π_i and q_{ij} in terms of λ, μ, ϕ, and ψ:

$$\pi_0 = \frac{\gamma(\lambda + \mu)}{\delta_1 + \delta_2 + \gamma(\lambda + \mu)}$$

$$\pi_1 = \frac{\delta_2}{\delta_1 + \delta_2 + \gamma(\lambda + \mu)} \tag{5}$$

$$\pi_2 = \frac{\delta_1}{\delta_1 + \delta_2 + \gamma(\lambda + \mu)}$$

and

$$Q = (q_{ij}) = \begin{pmatrix} 0 & \dfrac{\lambda\gamma}{\delta_2} & \dfrac{\mu\gamma}{\delta_1} \\[2ex] \dfrac{\phi\,\delta_2}{\gamma(\lambda + \mu)} & 0 & \dfrac{(1 - \phi)\,\delta_2}{\delta_1} \\[2ex] \dfrac{\psi\,\delta_1}{\gamma(\lambda + \mu)} & \dfrac{(1 - \psi)\,\delta_1}{\delta_2} & 0 \end{pmatrix} . \tag{6}$$

It will be noted that in the matrix (6) it is the columns rather than the rows which sum to unity, as a simple consequence of the definition of q_{ij}. In fact p_{ij} and q_{ij} represent corresponding conditional distributions.

It is not difficult to write the (unconditional) initial queue length probabilities in terms of Q. If

$\alpha_n = $ Prob (Northbound period begins with n queued), $n = 1, 2, \cdots$,

then the value $n = 1$ can arise in either of two ways: the northbound period follows an empty period (probability q_{01}) or it follows a southbound period in which only one northbound car has arrived. The probability of the arrival of n northbound cars in a southbound period of duration t is Poisson with parameter

λt, and therefore the unconditional probability of the arrival of n cars is

$$\int_0^\infty \frac{e^{-\lambda t}(\lambda t)^n}{n!}\, g(t)\, dt = \frac{\lambda^n(-1)^n}{n!}\, \psi^{(n)}, \qquad n = 0, 1, \ldots, \tag{7}$$

where index on ψ denotes differentiation

But, in considering a northbound period preceded by a south-bound period, we are specifically disallowing the possibility that no cars will arrive in the period, and therefore the probability (7) needs to be truncated by omitting $n = 0$, that is dividing by $1 - \psi$. Hence the distribution of queue length at the beginning of a north-bound period is

$$\alpha_1 = q_{01} - \frac{q_{21}\,\lambda\,\psi^{(1)}}{1 - \psi}$$

$$\alpha_n = q_{21}\,\frac{(-\lambda)^n\,\psi^{(n)}}{(1 - \psi)\,n!}. \tag{8}$$

Equations (6) and (8) express the queue length probabilities in terms of the duration Laplace transforms ϕ and ψ. However these same functions can be constructed by averaging the Laplace transform of Eq. (13), Section 2.6 over the distribution of r given by Eq. (8) above. It is not difficult[†] to show that the Laplace transform of the Borel-Tanner distribution is of the form

$$\phi(t; r) = e^{Cr} \tag{9}$$

where C is a function of ρ and t only, i.e., independent of r. Hence we have

$$\phi(t) = \sum_r e^{Cr}\, \alpha_r, \tag{10}$$

an equation in ϕ and ψ arising from consideration of northbound dominance periods. A similar equation holds for southbound dominance periods; from the two, ϕ and ψ are determined in principle.

---

† Haight, F. A. and Breuer, M. A., *Biometrika* **47**, 143–50 (1960).

6.9 The Rush Hour

The simplest results of queueing theory, which we have used extensively, relate to equilibrium or steady state behavior. We shall now point out briefly several aspects of the transient behavior of a $M/M/1$ queue. We do not specifically equate the $M/M/1$ case with any particular traffic situation; rather we use it as a generally applicable example (chosen for mathematical simplicity) of a traffic jam.

Traffic engineers are well aware of the patterns of traffic flow at particular locations and these daily (or at least periodic) cycles may be regarded, in places where cars accumulate, as values of the queue theoretic parameters λ and μ, dependent on time. If we go back to Eqs. (9) of Section 2.3, we need to introduce the idea of the number N in the queue at time zero, since transient results may depend on this quantity. Therefore we begin by writing the analogous set

$$
\left\{
\begin{aligned}
&\frac{\partial}{\partial t}\, p_{0,N}(t) = -\,\rho(t)\, p_{N,0} + p_0 \\[2mm]
&\frac{\partial}{\partial t}\, p_{n,N}(t) = -\,[1 + \rho(t)]\, p_{N,n} + \rho(t)\, p_{N,n-1} + p_{N,n+1} \qquad (1) \\[2mm]
&p_{N,n}(0) = \delta_{N,n},
\end{aligned}
\right.
$$

where

$$\delta_{N,n} = 1, \qquad n = N$$

$$\delta_{N,n} = 0, \qquad n \neq N.$$

Replacing $\rho(t)$ by

$$r(t) = \frac{1}{t}\int_0^t \rho(u)\, du \qquad (2)$$

which satisfies

$$tr' = \rho - r, \qquad (3)$$

and replacing $p_{N,n}$ by

$$q_{N,n}(t) = e^{t[1+r(t)]} \, p_{N,n}(t), \tag{4}$$

we can simplify Eq. (1) to the form

$$\begin{cases} \dfrac{\partial}{\partial t} q_{N,0} = q_{N,0} + q_{N,1} \\[2ex] \dfrac{\partial}{\partial t} q_{N,n} = \rho(t)\, q_{N,n-1} + q_{N,n+1} \\[2ex] q_{N,n}(0) = \delta_{N,n}. \end{cases} \tag{5}$$

The generating function

$$q_N(s, t) = \sum_{n=0}^{\infty} q_{N,n}(t) \frac{(s-t)^n}{n!} \tag{6}$$

is easily seen to satisfy the differential equation

$$\frac{\partial^2 q_N}{\partial t \, \partial s} = \rho \, q_N \tag{7}$$

which is well known in mathematical physics. Rather than embark on a solution of Eq. (7), the interest in which lies more in the theory of differential equations than in queueing theory, we merely remark that a solution (in terms of Bessel functions) exists and pass to the more useful question of mean and variance as functions of time.

Let

$$m_N(t) = \sum_{n=0}^{\infty} n \, p_{N,n}(t) \tag{8}$$

and

$$v_N(t) = \sum_{n=0}^{\infty} (n - m_N(t))^2 \, p_{N,n}(t). \tag{9}$$

Differentiating with respect to t, we obtain

$$\frac{\partial}{\partial t} m_N(t) = \rho(t) - 1 + p_{N,0} \tag{10}$$

and

$$\frac{\partial}{\partial t} v_N(t) = 2\left[\rho(t) + \rho(t)\, m_N(t) - m_N(t)\right] - \left[1 + 2m_N(t)\right] \frac{\partial m_N(t)}{\partial t}. \quad (11)$$

Therefore, $m_N(t)$ satisfies

$$m_N(t) = \left[r(t) - 1\right]t + \int_0^t p_{N,0}(u)\, du + N. \quad (12)$$

and $v_N(t)$ satisfies

$$v_N(t) = 2\int_0^t \{\rho(u) + [\rho(u) - 1]m_N(u)\}\, du - m_N(t) - \quad (13)$$

$$[m_N(t)]^2 + N + N^2.$$

The only obstacle to the evaluation of (12) and hence (13) is the integral

$$\int_0^t p_{N,0}(u)\, du. \quad (14)$$

If the values of N, t, and ρ are such that the probability of the queue vanishing before time t can be neglected, the integral (14) vanishes.[†] For $\rho > 1$ and constant we obtain the approximations

$$m_N(t) \approx N + t[\rho(t) - 1] \quad (15)$$

and

$$v_N(t) \approx (\rho + 1)t. \quad (16)$$

It is not difficult to obtain similar formulas relating to other transient characteristics of a queue. In Section 6.10 we shall give several references to such results, none of which seem yet to have been applied to road traffic congestion.

[†] Actually its value is $\rho^{-N}(1 - \rho)^{-1} + o(1)$ for ρ constant and > 1.

6.10 Comment

Section 6.2 offers a formulation due to Uematu [25] which seems to be the only deductive approach to the problem. There have been a number of quasi-scientific attempts to rationalize signal settings, of which references [19] and [28] are typical. Morgan's ideas [19a] on the subject are a mixture of empiricism, deduction and operations research, and consequently quite useful.

The left turning model of Section 6.3 is a slight generalization of Newell's [21].

The results in the first part of Section 6.4 are well known in renewal theory; the paper of Cox and Smith [5] contains in essence the argument we have used. A more generalized treatment (non-homogeneous lanes) is due to Weiss and Maradudin [26a]. The study of traffic dynamics for multilane highways has been initiated by Gazis and Herman [10]. Other aspects of parallel traffic queues are contained in papers by Edie [8] and Haight [13]. The latter paper deals with the problem of joining the shorter of two queues and has recently been improved by Kingman [17]. (cf. also Wilkins [27]). Edie's work is operations research at its best and shows how theories can be usefully applied.

The signal sequence model of Section 6.5 is also due to Newell [22]. Burke [3] treats the general problem of queue output, as exemplified in our Eq. (2).

A parking lot, as formulated in Section 6.6, is the mathematical equivalent of a telephone switchboard in which the slots are lines, cars are calls and parking time is holding time. There is an enormous literature on the subject; equations such as (7) have been applied since early in the century [2, 9]. The specific parking aspects are due to Haight and Jacobson [12]. Kometani and Kato [18] and Mori [20] furnish some empirical support for the distribution theoretic assumptions of the telephone switchboard analogy.

The earliest paper on merging is due to Ho [14] and contains a rather unrealistic model. Most of the mathematics presented in Section 6.7 derives from the paper of Haight et al. [11] although some of the ideas occur in a thesis of Huemer [15]. Oliver [23] treats the problem of symmetrical merging (in which neither lane has priority) in a perfectly queue theoretic manner. Bisbee [1] deals with merging of objects in greater generality, so as to include aircraft and assembly line problems.

The bottleneck problem and its solution is due to Tanner, whose paper [24] on this subject carries the analysis much further than we have done. There may in fact be a new method of treating the whole delay question of Chapter 5 concealed in Tanner's rather difficult equations. Furthermore, Tanner defines, but does not discuss, two other cases in which the time to transit the bottleneck exceeds the allowable headway in one or in both directions. Mr. Vanolin Hurdle has pointed out to me that these models are essentially equivalent, respectively, to a yield sign on the minor road and to a four way stop sign.

Transient behavior of queues has been studied by numerous authors of whom Volberg [26] is noteworthy. The treatment which we give is based on a paper of Clarke [4] and Section 3.1 of the book by Cox and Smith [6]. The reader will find numerous applications of these and other formulas in the expository paper of Cox [7]. The exact transient solution for the $M/M/1$ case, Eq. (9), Section 2.3, when both λ and μ are time dependent, is given in very compact form by Sonnenschein [23a].

REFERENCES

1. Bisbee, E. F., Secondary Flows in Traffic Streams. Ph. D. Thesis. Univ. of California, Berkeley, California, 1962.
2. Brockmeyer, E., Halstrøm, H. L., and Jensen, A., The Life and Works of A. K. Erlang. Copenhagen Telephone Co. Copenhagen, 1948.
3. Burke, P. J., The Output of a Queueing System. *Operations Research* 4, No. 6, 699–704 (Dec. 1956).
4. Clarke, A. B., A Waiting Line Process of Markov Type. *Ann. Math. Statist.* 27, No. 2, 452–459 (1956).
5. Cox, D. R., and Smith, W. L., Superposition of Renewal Processes. *Biometrika* 41, 91–99 (1954).
6. Cox, D. R., and Smith, W. L., "Queues." Wiley, New York 1961.
7. Cox, D. R., The Statistical Analysis of Congestion. *J. Roy. Statist. Soc.* Ser. A, 118, 324–35 (1955).

8. Edie, L. C., Traffic Delays at Toll Booths. *In* "Operations Research for Management," Vol. II, pp. 20–56. Johns Hopkins Press, Baltimore, Maryland, 1956; *Operations Research* **2**, No. 2, 107–38 (1954).

9. Fry, Thornton C., "Probability and its Engineering Uses." Van Nostrand, New York 1928.

10. Gazis, D. C., Herman, R., and Weiss, G., Density Oscillations Between Lanes of a Multilane Highway. *Operations Research* **10**, 658–67 (1962).

11. Haight, F. A., Bisbee, E. F., and Wojcik, C., Some Mathematical Aspects of the Problem of Merging. *Highway Research Board Bull.* No. 356 (1962).

12. Haight, F. A., and Jacobson, A. S., Some Mathematical Aspects of the Parking Problem. *Proc. Highway Research Board* **41**, 363–74 (1962).

13. Haight, F. A., Two Queues in Parallel. *Biometrika* **45**, Parts 3 and 4, 401–10 (Dec. 1958).

14. Ho, Er-Chun, A Statistical Analysis of Congested Merging Traffic. *In* "Analysis and Simulation of Vehicular Traffic Flow" (D. L. Trautman, Harold Davis, J. Heilfron, Er-Chun Ho, J. H. Mathewson, and A. Rosenbloom.). Inst. of Transportation and Traffic Eng. Research Report No. 20, Univ. of California, Los Angeles, California.

15. Huemer, D. A., The Monte Carlo Method. M. A. Thesis. Claremont College, California (1961).

16. Hunt, G. C., Sequential Arrays of Waiting Lines. *Operations Research* **4**, No. 6, 674–683 (Dec. 1956).

17. Kingman, J. F. C., Two Similar Queues in Parallel. *Ann. Math. Statist.* **32**, No. 4, 1314–1323 (Dec. 1961).

18. Kometani, E., and Kato, A., On the Theoretical Capacity of an Off-Street Parking Space. *Mem. Fac. Eng. Kyoto Univ.* **18**, No. 4, 315–328 (Oct. 1956).

19. La Vallee, R. W., Scheduling of Traffic Signals by Linear Programming. *Proc. Highway Research Board* **35**, 534–542 (1956).

19a. Morgan, J. T., Synchronized Traffic Signals (unpublished).

20. Mori, M., Statistical Analysis of Parking Phenomena. *Mem. Fac. Eng. Osaka Univ.* **1**, 123–132 (Dec. 1959).

21. Newell, G. F., The Effect of Left Turns on the Capacity of a Traffic Intersection. *Quart. Appl. Math.* **17**, No. 1, 67–76 (April 1959).

22. Newell, G. F., The Flow of Highway Traffic Through a Sequence of Synchronized Traffic Signals. *Operations Research* **8**, No. 3, 390–405 (May-June 1960).

23. Oliver, R. M., On High-Speed Two-Lane Traffic Merges (to appear).

23a. Sonnenschein, J., Eléments de Solution du Comportement Transitoire d'une File d'attente simple lorsque l'intensité du Trafic depend du Temps. *Cahiers du Centre D'Études de Recherche Operationelle* **4**, No. 2, 117–8 (1962).

24. Tanner, J. C., A Problem of Interference Between Two Queues. *Biometrika* **40**, 58–69 (1953).

25. Uematu, T., On the Traffic Control at an Intersection Controlled by the Repeated Fixed-Cycle Traffic Light. *Ann. Inst. Statist. Math. Tokyo* **9**, 87–107 (1958).

26. Volberg, O., Probleme de la Queue Stationnaire et Non-stationnaire. *Compt. rend. acad. sci. U.R.S.S.* **24**, 657–661 (1939).

26a. Weiss, G. H., and Maradudin, A. A., Some Problems in Traffic Delay. *Operations Research* **10**, No. 1, 74–104 (Feb. 1962).

27. Wilkins, C. A., On Two Queues in Parallel. *Biometrika* **47**, Parts 1 and 2, 198–199 (June 1960).

28. Yablonskii, S. V., Gil'man, A. M., Kotel'nikov, I. V., and Potylitsyn, P. M., A Device for the Investigation of Street-Traffic Control Algorithms. *Soviet Physics Doklady* **5**, No. 3, 474–476 (Nov.-Dec. 1960).

CHAPTER 7

A Two Lane Road

7.1 Introduction

Throughout this chapter we will study a two lane homogeneous road in statistical equilibrium. Vehicles will be identical in every respect except their *free speed* V, a non-negative number which denotes the constant unobstructed speed of the vehicle. Whenever a car comes within a certain fixed distance of another car traveling in the same direction, the faster car will instantly assume the speed of the slower car and maintain that speed (or whatever speed the leading car is constrained to assume) for a period of time (possibly zero) until an *opportunity to pass* occurs. When such an opportunity exists, the following car instantly resumes its free speed, goes around the leading car, and comes back into the lane ahead of it.

The history of a particular car can be divided into periods during which it is traveling at its free speed (when it will be called a *leader*) and periods during which it is traveling at a slower speed (as a *follower*). The instant at which a car changes from leader to follower is called the moment of *overtaking* (in British usage, catching up) and the instant at which a car changes from follower to leader is called the moment of *passing* (in British usage, overtaking).

Each leader defines a moving queue, consisting at least of itself, and possibly of following vehicles. From one point of view, the leader might be considered the service mechanism, and the followers the queueing objects; alternatively one may consider the whole collection of leader and followers to be the queued items and the oncoming traffic to be the service mechanism. In any case, if T is the time for passing (which of course depends on the speeds

199

of leader and follower) time spent as follower is quite similar to the delay time treated in Chapter 5. We shall therefore, in the following mathematical formulation, take the results of Chapter 5 for granted, and perhaps even suppose that those results are perfect enough to specify a particular delay distribution as a function of the time required to pass and the oncoming traffic process.

The density of traffic will be denoted by λ, or in cases where the northbound and southbound traffic densities differ, by λ and λ'.[†] The basic problem, as far as an individual vehicle is concerned, is to determine his average speed as a function of V and λ. We have made some conjectures regarding this function in Chapter 3, but now wish to apply the more precise results which have been subsequently obtained. Various other problems, such as the frequency of passing, percent of time following, number of vehicles passed in unit time, etc., seem to hinge on this basic one.

There is another category of problems, which deal with the whole collection of vehicles. As we have pointed out in Section 3.2, there are many averages which may be considered, and for each of these we now introduce the corresponding statistical distribution. Questions about the average behavior of the collection again depend on the average behavior of a single car.

In this chapter we will first elaborate the very general model described above, point out some of the difficulties inherent in it, and deduce a few general formulas. Then a number of special cases will be treated. These particular two lane road models vary from the most primitive possible situations which may in any sense be regarded as road traffic to systems only slightly less general than the main formulation. We will take them up in increasing order of complexity, and therefore expect decreasingly exact results. Only when the postulates are most stringent is it possible to solve a few of the problems just mentioned, and even then the formulas are rather formidable.

[†] Not, as in Chapter 3, $\lambda' = \lambda_{max}$.

7.2 Various Speed Distributions

Consider a single vehicle of free speed V. In the course of time it will travel at many different speeds $(< V)$, and it is therefore appropriate to speak of the distribution of speeds for a single car. However, it should be clear that we mean a distribution with respect to time, rather than space, for it is only with such a definition that the mean value of the speed distribution will be equal to the average speed of the journey. Hence the speed distribution for a car of free speed V is of the form

$$g(u|V) = \delta(u - V)\,\alpha(V) + h(u|V), \qquad 0 < u \leqslant V \tag{1}$$

where

$$\delta(x) = \begin{cases} 0 & x \neq 0 \\ 1 & x = 0, \end{cases} \tag{2}$$

$\alpha(V)$ is the proportion of *time* that a car of free speed V will spend leading, and

$$\int_0^x h(u|x)\,du = 1 - \alpha(x). \tag{3}$$

We will assume that $\alpha(0) = 1$, $\alpha(\infty) = 0$, and that for $V_1 < V_2$, $\alpha(V_1) > \alpha(V_2)$, so that any increase in free speed leads to a decrease in proportion of time spent at free speed. For fixed V, let the mean of the distribution (1) be $m(V)$. In accordance with the arguments and notation of Chapter 3, we shall write $L = m(\infty)$, and naturally $m(0) = 0$. Multiplying Eq. (1) by u and integrating, we obtain

$$m(V) = V\,\alpha(V) + s(V) \tag{4}$$

where

$$s(V) = \int_0^V u\,h(u|V)\,du \tag{5}$$

is the mean distance covered by a car of free speed V as a follower during a unit of time.

Now consider the whole collection of vehicles. Let the free speed[†] satisfy

$$F_0(u) = \text{Prob (Free speed} < u), \qquad \frac{d}{du} F_0(u) = f_0(u) \qquad (6)$$

with mean value m_0. Furthermore, let the distribution of mean speeds be

$$F(u) = \text{Prob (mean speed} < u), \qquad \frac{d}{du} F(u) = f(u). \qquad (7)$$

If it were possible to register the instantaneous speed of each car at a given moment (which we assume to be a typical moment, since the system is in equilibrium), the distribution obtained would be

$$g(u) = \int_0^\infty g(u|v) f_0(v) \, dv. \qquad (8)$$

It is easy to see that the distributions $f(x)$ and $g(x)$ share the same mean value. For the mean of $f(x)$ is

$$\int_0^\infty m(x) f_0(x) \, dx = \int_0^\infty f_0(x) \int_0^x v \, g(v|x) \, dv \, dx$$

and of $g(x)$ is

$$\int_0^\infty u \, g(u) \, du = \int_0^\infty u \int_u^\infty g(u|x) f_0(x) \, dx \, du,$$

and the same triangular domain of integration is specified by both double integrals. This common mean will be denoted by m.

Next, we consider the subpopulations of leaders and followers. The instantaneous speed distribution of leaders is, using Bayes' Theorem

---

† True (space measured) free speed, cf. Section 4.7.

$$\text{Prob }(x|\text{leader}) = \frac{\text{Prob }(\text{leader}|x)\, f_0(x)}{\text{Prob }(\text{leader})} = \mu\,\alpha(x)\,f_0(x), \qquad (9)$$

where μ = mean queue length is the reciprocal of Prob (leader). Similarly the distribution of free speeds of followers is

$$\frac{[1 - \alpha(x)]\, f_0(x)}{1 - 1/\mu} \qquad (10)$$

and of instantaneous speeds of followers is

$$\frac{\alpha(x)\, f_0(x)\, [\mu(x) - 1]}{1 - 1/\mu} \qquad (11)$$

where $\mu(V)$ is the mean queue length of queues of speed V. This quantity is connected with μ by means of the relation (9); hence

$$\mu = \int_0^\infty \mu\,\mu(x)\,\alpha(x)\,f_0(x)\,dx,$$

which shows that

$$g(x) = \mu(x)\,\alpha(x)\,f_0(x) \qquad (12)$$

is an honest probability distribution. Moreover, since $1/\mu$ is the probability that a car is a leader,

$$\int_0^\infty \alpha(x)\,f_0(x)\,dx = 1/\mu. \qquad (13)$$

Finally, the mean speed of leaders, which we denote by M, is given by

$$M = \int_0^\infty x\,\mu\,\alpha(x)\,f_0(x)\,dx. \qquad (14)$$

The reader may wish to apply the foregoing results to the following simple example. Imagine the system to consist of cars with free speeds 40, 50, and 60, arranged at a typical moment into five queues:

50	50	40	40	40
60	60	50	50	50
60		50	50	50
60		60		50
		60		60
				60

each of which is supposed to be proceeding up the page at the speed of the queue leader. Then

$$f_0(x) = \begin{cases} 3/20, & x = 40 \\ 9/20, & x = 50 \\ 8/20, & x = 60 \end{cases}$$

$\alpha(40) = 1 \qquad m(40) = 40 \qquad \mu(40) = 14/3 \qquad\qquad g(40) = 7/10$

$\alpha(50) = 2/9 \quad m(50) = 380/9 \quad \mu(50) = 3 \qquad\qquad g(50) = 3/10$

$\alpha(60) = 0 \qquad m(60) = 45 \qquad\qquad \mu = 4, \qquad m = 43, \qquad M = 44.$

Now, suppose a speed distribution is formed from the speeds of northbound cars passing a point,[†] where the point is moving with speed V, $-\infty < V < \infty$. If the distribution of speeds is $g_V(x)$, then we have, by Eq. (2) of Section 4.7,

$$g_V(x) = \frac{|V - x| \, g(x)}{\displaystyle\int_0^\infty |V - u| g(u) \, du}, \qquad 0 < x < \infty. \tag{15}$$

When the distribution formed is constrained by some other condition, the function $g(x)$ in Eq. (15) must be replaced by the appropriate distribution. Suppose, for example, a point with speed V is used to form the speed distribution of all cars going more slowly than V. The distribution of speeds conditional on $X < V$ is simply

$$\frac{g(x)}{\int_0^V g(u) \, du}, \qquad 0 < x < V. \tag{16}$$

---

† Or vehicle on a separate track.

Replacing $g(x)$ in Eq. (15) by this expression, we obtain a formula similar to (15), but with the domain (and limits of integration) reduced from $(0, \infty)$ to $(0, V)$.

The function $g(x)$ in Eq. (16) can also be modified in various ways. If we want the distribution of leaders only, as it appears to a .car of a free speed V, we would find it to be

$$\frac{|V - x|\, \alpha(x)\, f_0(x)}{\int_0^\infty |V - u|\, \alpha(u)\, f_0(u)\, du}, \qquad 0 < x < \infty. \tag{17}$$

Consequently the distribution of speeds of leaders, as recorded by a stationary road tape, is

$$x\, \alpha(x)\, f_0(x)\, (\mu/M). \tag{18}$$

Finally, the distribution of speeds of leaders who travel more slowly than a vehicle of speed V, as it appears to that vehicle is

$$\frac{(V - x)\, \alpha(x)\, f_0(x)}{\int_0^V (V - u)\, \alpha(u)\, f_0(u)\, du}, \qquad 0 < x < V. \tag{19}$$

This is the distribution of speed of the next queue overtaken by a passing vehicle of free speed V. In this application, the assumption of a separate track for the observing vehicle is nugatory, since only a single overtaking is postulated.

7.3 Typical Cycle for a Vehicle

By a cycle for a vehicle, we mean the time between consecutive passings; the average experience of a car is its experience over an average cycle. That story may be very complex, since it depends on the random variables characterizing oncoming (southbound) traffic as well as those derived from northbound cars encountered in the course of the cycle. Suppose the free speed of the car under investigation is V; first consider passing.

Passing will be classified under one of three headings: (a) *simple* passing, in which the first car overtaken is a leader, with speed distribution of Eq. (19), Section 7.2, and is passed while this car remains a leader, (b) *compound* passing, in which a queue of $k > 1$ cars is overtaken, traveling a speed distributed as Eq. (19) and in which the test car will pass after $k - 1$ other passings, but while following will always follow at the same speed, and (c) *complex* passing, in which the car first overtaken overtakes another before being passed, and this one also overtakes before the queue is cleared, etc. In the most general case (complex passing), the test car, during a cycle, travels at speeds $V > X_1 > X_2 > \ldots > X_n$ before resuming its free speed V. If the mean values of the distributions of these speeds were known, together with the mean duration of following for each of them, the average speed over the cycle could be computed as simply

$$\text{Mean speed} = \frac{\sum_{i=0}^{n} \bar{X}_i \bar{t}_i}{\sum_{i=0}^{n} \bar{t}_i} \tag{1}$$

where $V = X_0$, t_i is the time spent following at speed X_i, and bars denote mean values.

It is easy to find the distributions of the variables $X_1, \ldots, X_n$ by using Eq. (19) of Section 7.2. With the convenient abbreviations

$$\beta(x) = \alpha(x) f_0(x) \quad \text{and} \quad C^{-1} = \int_0^V (V - u)\, \beta(u)\, du,$$

the distribution of X_1 is

$$C\,(V - x)\, \beta(x), \qquad 0 < x < V. \tag{2}$$

Also the distribution of $X_2|X_1$ is

$$\frac{(X_1 - x)\, \beta(x)}{\int_0^{X_1} (X_1 - u)\, \beta(u)\, du}, \qquad 0 < x < X_1 \tag{3}$$

and therefore the distribution of X_2 is

$$\int_0^V \frac{(V - x_1)\beta(x_1)(x_1 - x)\beta(x)}{\int_0^V (V - u)\beta(u)\, du \int_0^{x_1}(x_1 - u)\beta(u)\, du}\, dx_1 \tag{4}$$

$$= C(a_2 - b_2\, x)\beta(x), \qquad 0 < x < V.$$

Continuing this process, we arrive at the general result

$$C(a_j - b_j x) \beta(x), \qquad 0 < x < V, \tag{5}$$

for the distribution of X_j, where the coefficients a_j and b_j are given by the recurrence relations

$$a_j = \int_0^V \frac{y \, \beta(y) \, (a_{j-1} - y \, b_{j-1})}{\int_0^y (y - u) \, \beta(u) \, du} \, dy \tag{6}$$

$$b_j = \int_0^V \frac{\beta(y) \, (a_{j-1} - y \, b_{j-1})}{\int_0^y (y - u) \, \beta(u) \, du} \, dy \tag{7}$$

and where $a_1 = V$, $b_1 = 1$.

The quantity n is also random variable about which nothing is known at present. Note: it is not the queue length.

Next we shall consider in detail a simple passing. If the leading vehicle has speed X and the following vehicle free speed V, then the maneuver will require space (in the oncoming lane) $cV/(V - X)$ and time $c/(V - X)$ where c is the constant sum of spacing required before and after the passing vehicle resumes its proper lane. Knowing these fractions, we can apply the results of Chapter 5 for appropriate southbound traffic and obtain the distribution of delay. As we have seen in that chapter, the problem will yield no simple solution unless the southbound traffic is of a particularly simple form. In the ideal situation we would wish to assume that it was subject to the same rules as the northbound traffic.

Two plausible simplifying conjectures have been suggested.

(a) *Carleson's hypothesis.*[†] In the simple passing of a car of free speed X by a car of free speed V, the distance followed is proportional to the distance required to pass. Thus the distance followed is of the form

$$\frac{kV}{V - X} \tag{8}$$

[†] Note: not all of Carleson's work is dependent on this hypothesis, cf. Section 7.6.

and the time following is

$$\frac{kV}{X(V-X)}. \tag{9}$$

(b) *Hypothesis of equal delay.* Suppose the delay due to a simple passing is independent of the relative speed of vehicles, i.e., a large speed differential yields large delay per unit time for a few time units, while a small speed differential yields small delay per unit time for many time units. Then, letting the time following be t, the distance covered while following would be Xt while a distance Vt could have been covered. Thus the following car has been delayed a distance $(V-X)t$, which it will take a time $(V-X)t/V = \text{const.}$ to traverse. Solving for t, we have

$$\frac{kV}{V-X} \tag{10}$$

for the time spent following, and

$$\frac{kVX}{V-X} \tag{11}$$

for the distance.

One way to compare the relative merits of (9) and (10) is to see how they behave in limiting cases. If $V \to \infty$, (9) states that the following time will be inversely proportional to the speed of the car followed, while (10) implies that the following time will be independent of this speed, and will therefore depend only on the conditions of southbound traffic. The most particular argument favoring the hypothesis of equal delay will be found by setting $X = 0$ in Eqs. (8) and (11).

The discussion thus far applies to simple passing. For compound passing of a vehicle of free speed X, by a vehicle of free speed V, it is necessary to apply our results to each of the intermediate vehicles, supposing passing to take place from the head of the queue. If these vehicles have free speeds $U_1, \ldots, U_p$, then the distribution of U_j can be calculated in very much the same way as Eq. (19), Section 7.2. Namely, the distribution is that of leading vehicles with free speeds below X, as appearing to a vehicle of speed X. In this case, n will indeed be queue length.

7.4 Zero-One Model

We begin the treatment of specific two lane road models with a very simple system. Suppose there are two types of cars, *slow* cars, which have identical finite speeds, and *fast* cars, which have infinite speed. Let all car lengths be zero, and let the spacing of slow cars be random with parameter λ. Suppose further that the density of fast cars is so small that we can assume that queues of three or more are impossible without introducing substantial error.

Let the probability that a slow car is followed by one fast car be p. Clearly, fast cars are also arranged randomly with parameter $p\lambda$. However, a moment's thought about the gap distribution for all cars (which contains a spike at the origin) will show that the over-all vehicular arrangement cannot be random. Furthermore, it does not even have independent gaps, for following each fast car must be a slow car. We have the simple set of transition probabilities:

Prob (zero gap|preceding gap finite) $= p$

Prob (finite gap|preceding gap finite) $= 1 - p$

Prob (zero gap|preceding gap zero) $= 0$

Prob (finite gap|preceding gap zero) $= 1$.

It is interesting to compare this model with the various queueing models proposed. Since the zero-one queue length cannot be geometric or Borel by any choice of parameters, the Independent Traffic Queueing Model and Efflux Traffic Queueing Model of Section 4.6 cannot apply. The Random Traffic Queueing Model of Section 6.5 is more to the point, and in fact differs from the zero-one model only in the passing mechanism proposed. In the former case, it was assumed that cars passed at random, independently of each other and of the other queues and of the southbound stream. Now we assume nothing about the passing mechanism except that it sweeps down the stream, offering exactly the same opportunity to every queue.

Consider the relative frequency of zero and negative exponential gaps. Since the relative abundance of fast to slow cars is p, the probability that a car chosen at random is fast is $p/(1 + p)$. The probabilities of zero and negative exponential gaps are therefore $p/(1 + p)$ and $1/(1 + p)$ respectively, and we may write [cf. Eq. (1), Section 4.6]

$$g(x) = \frac{p}{1 + p} \, \delta(x) + \frac{\lambda \, e^{-\lambda x}}{1 + p}. \tag{1}$$

Although Eq. (1) has the same form as the independent gap distributions which we have discussed in such detail in Chapter 4, it has a totally different meaning, and cannot be used with the equations of Section 4.3 to find the counting distribution. We can obtain the counting distribution by using the differential-difference equation method (Section 2.3) with $p_n(\tau)$ denoting the probability of a count of n vehicles in time τ.[†]

Since

Probability of no cars in $\Delta \tau = (1 - \lambda) \, \Delta \tau + o(\Delta \tau)$

Probability of one car in $\Delta \tau = (1 - p) \, \lambda \, \Delta \tau + o(\Delta \tau)$

Probability of two cars in $\Delta \tau = p \lambda \, \Delta \tau + o(\Delta \tau)$

Probability of > two cars in $\Delta \tau = o(\Delta \tau)$

we easily obtain the equations

$$\frac{\partial p_n(\tau)}{\partial \tau} = - \lambda p_n(\tau) + \lambda(1 - p)p_{n-1}(\tau) + p \lambda p_{n-2}(\tau), \qquad n = 0, 1, \ldots$$

$$\tag{2}$$

where, as usual, $p_n(\tau) = 0$ whenever $n < 0$. We are now not interested in setting the partial derivatives equal to zero, as in

---

[†] The question of synchronous or asynchronous counting does not arise since all finite gaps are negative exponential, and we expressly include queues of two in the basic formulation.

Section 2.3, for the variable is not elapsed time but length of a counting interval.   The set of equations (2) can be solved successively, and yield

$$p_n(\tau) = e^{-\lambda\tau} \sum_{i=N}^{n} \frac{p^{n-i}(1-p)^{2i-n}(\lambda\tau)^i}{(n-i)!\,(2i-n)!},$$ (3)

where N is the integral part of $\frac{1}{2}(n+1)$.

Equation (3) may be compared directly with the (incorrect) result which would have been obtained if we had (mistakenly) assumed Eq. (1) to represent the density for independent gaps. The (erroneous) counting distribution would be Eq. (10) of Section 4.6 with $\Delta = 0$, $k = 1$ and $\mu = \lambda$.

In this section we have mentioned neither the frequency of the opportunity to pass, nor its relationship with the southbound stream, and cannot therefore compute the mean speed of fast cars. We leave that question to be taken up in the context of more sophisticated models.

7.5 Isoveloxic Traffic

Suppose all northbound vehicles travel at exactly the same speed U, with the exception of a single northbound *test car* which has a free speed $V > U$. Suppose further that the cars are arranged as an independent (D, M) traffic queueing model (cf. Section 4.6) with density λ, flow ρ and minimum spacing Δ. The distribution of queue length is geometric and therefore the mean queue length is

$$\mu = \frac{1}{1-\lambda\Delta}$$ (1)

in cars, and is

$$\frac{\Delta}{1-\lambda\Delta}$$ (2)

in space, and is

$$\frac{\varDelta/U}{1-\lambda\varDelta} \tag{3}$$

in time. Also, the mean distance between queues is $(1/\lambda)$.[†]

The test car, gaining at speed $(V-U)$ on a queue as well as on the space between queues, will require time

$$\frac{\dfrac{\varDelta}{1-\lambda\varDelta}+\dfrac{1}{\lambda}}{V-U} \tag{4}$$

to complete the free speed portion of a typical cycle. If W is the average waiting time (traveling at speed U) and m the mean speed achieved, then we obtain by simple calculation

$$m = \frac{\lambda\,U\,W\,(V-U)\,(1-\lambda\varDelta)+V}{\lambda\,W\,(V-U)\,(1-\lambda\varDelta)+1}. \tag{5}$$

This fraction reduces to the value V in the following special cases: $U=V$ (no attempt to pass) and $\lambda\varDelta=1$ (jampacked road).

The problem of finding m is now reduced to a problem of finding W. Before performing this calculation, however, we will combine Eq. (5) with the two conjectured forms for W as given in Eq. (9) and (10) of Section 7.3. Since these expressions were supposed to apply to simple passing, we will multiply them by the mean queue length before substituting into Eq. (5).

Carleson's hypothesis yields

$$W = \frac{kV}{U}\frac{1}{V-U}\frac{1}{1-\lambda\varDelta}, \tag{6}$$

where k is a constant having no intuitive significance[‡] but of the

---

[†] It may appear paradoxical that the mean distance between traffic queues is exactly the same as the mean spacing. However, the spacing associated with consecutive cars in different queues is not the distance between the queues; the former is measured nose to nose and the latter nose to tail. Therefore they differ by exactly $\varDelta$.

[‡] For infinite V, k represents (WU/μ).

dimensionality of $\varDelta$, distance per car. The corresponding value of m is

$$m = UV\frac{1 + k\lambda}{U + k\lambda V}. \tag{7}$$

Eq. (7) gives sensible results in certain limiting cases: if $V \to U$, then $m \to V$; if $V \to \infty$, we obtain

$$m_{\max} = U\frac{\lambda k + 1}{\lambda k}. \tag{8}$$

However, if we stop the northbound traffic altogether by setting $U = 0$, we find that the test car is also stopped, a result which is not quite right. The reason for this state of affairs is plain enough; Carleson's hypothesis itself shares the same disadvantage, and Eq. (6) is independent of the southbound stream. Hence it is unreasonable to expect variation in U (or in λ) to yield meaningful results. In fact we note that $\lambda = 0$ gives a correct value, but $\lambda = \lambda_{\max} = (1/\varDelta)$ does not.

The hypothesis of equal delay leads to the formula

$$m = V\frac{1 + k\lambda U}{1 + k\lambda V}, \tag{9}$$

a result very much resembling Eq. (7). In this case, k is of the dimension of W, and $U = 0$ yields a perfectly consistent value for m.

Next we will show how to obtain the average delay due to a simple passing from the results of Chapter 5. The same queueing model, with parameters λ' and U', will be used for the southbound stream. It is easy to see that this structure provides the test car with time gaps having the gap distribution[†] [cf. Section 4.6, Eq. (5)]

$$g(x) = p\,\delta(x - \sigma) + q\,\beta\,e^{-\beta(x - \sigma)} \tag{10}$$

[†] Hence the choice of this model; the efflux traffic queueing model (Section 4.6) and the random traffic queueing model (Section 6.5) do not have gap distributions.

for suitable values of p, q, σ, and β. Since the southbound traffic approaches the test car at a speed $(V + U')$, and since the mean queue length for southbound vehicles is $(1 - \lambda'\varDelta)^{-1}$, we have

$$p = \lambda'\varDelta, \qquad q = 1 - \lambda'\varDelta \qquad (11)$$

for the probabilities of long and short gaps respectively,

$$\sigma = \frac{\varDelta}{V + U'} \qquad (12)$$

for the duration of short gaps and

$$\beta = \lambda'(V + U') \qquad (13)$$

for the reciprocal mean duration of long gaps. Allowing passing cars one augmented car length for the maneuver, we can dispense with an awkward constant and write

$$T = \frac{\varDelta}{V - U} > \sigma. \qquad (14)$$

for the time required to pass. The distribution (10) has cumulative form

$$G(x) = \begin{cases} 1 - q\,e^{-\beta(x-\sigma)}, & x > \sigma \\ 0 & x < \sigma \end{cases} \qquad (15)$$

and mean value

$$p\sigma + (q/\beta)(1 - \beta\sigma). \qquad (16)$$

The corresponding starting density is

$$g_0(x) = \begin{cases} \dfrac{q\,\beta}{q + \sigma\beta\,e^{-\beta(x-\sigma)}}, & x > \sigma \\[2ex] \dfrac{\beta}{q + \sigma\beta}, & x < \sigma \end{cases} \qquad (17)$$

with cumulative form

$$G_0(x) = \begin{cases} 1 - \dfrac{q}{q + \sigma\beta\,e^{-\beta(x-\sigma)}}, & x > \sigma \\[2ex] \dfrac{\beta x}{q + \sigma\beta}, & x < \sigma. \end{cases} \qquad (18)$$

Substituting these values into Eq. (11) of Section 5.2, we obtain, after integration and simplification,

Mean delay for simple passing   (19)

$$= \frac{\sigma^2 \beta}{2} - \frac{1 + \beta T + p\beta\sigma}{\beta} + \frac{\exp \beta(T - \sigma)}{q\beta}.$$

Substituting the original constants from Eqs. (11), (12), (13), and (14), and going over to compound passing, we find that

$$W = \frac{\exp\left[\varDelta\lambda' \dfrac{U + U'}{V - U}\right]}{(1 - \lambda'\varDelta)(1 - \lambda\varDelta)(\lambda')(V + U')} - \tag{20}$$

$$\frac{(\varDelta\lambda')^2(V - U) + 2(V - U + \varDelta\lambda' V + \varDelta\lambda' U')}{(1 - \lambda\varDelta)(2\lambda')(V + U')(V - U)}.$$

7.6 Distributed Speeds; Following Time Conjectures

We return to the more general situation characterized by a free speed distribution $f_0(x)$, and are now quite unable to find a formula for W. Instead, we will use some of the preceding results to make more sophisticated conjectures. The density of cars of speed X is

$$\rho/m(X) \tag{1}$$

and these are passed, on the average, by a car of free speed V with frequency

$$\rho(V, X) = \rho \frac{m(V) - m(X)}{m(X)}, \qquad V > X. \tag{2}$$

The function $\alpha(V)$, defined in Section 7.2, can be expressed in terms of $\rho(V, X)$ by means of the relation

$$1 - \alpha(V) = \int_0^V \rho(V, x)\, W\, f_0(x)\, dx, \tag{3}$$

where W is as defined in Section 7.5, and has one or several arguments depending on which following time conjecture we are willing to make. Similarly, the quantity $s(V)$ of Section 7.2 can be written

$$s(V) = \int_0^V \rho(V, x)\, x\, W\, f_0(x)\, dx. \tag{4}$$

If we combine Eqs. (2), (3), and (4) above with Eq. (4) of Section 7.2, we obtain an integral equation in $m(V)$, namely

$$m(V) = V - \int_0^V (V - x)\, \rho(V, x)\, W\, f_0(x)\, dx. \tag{5}$$

Carleson's hypothesis. Replacing W by the value given in Eq. (6), Section 7.5, U now being x, and writing $\phi(x) = [m(x)]^{-1}$, we find that

$$V\, \phi(V) - \frac{\rho\, k\, V}{1 - \lambda \Delta} \int_0^V [\phi(x) - \phi(V)] \frac{f_0(x)}{x}\, dx = 1. \tag{6}$$

Let new functions $a(x)$, $A(x)$, and $\psi(x)$ be defined by[†]

$$a(x) = \frac{\rho k\, f_0(x)}{(1 - \lambda\Delta)\, x}, \qquad A(x) = \int_0^x a(t)\, dt, \qquad \phi(x) = \frac{1}{x} + \psi(x),$$

$$\psi(0) = 0. \tag{7}$$

Then we can write Eq. (6) in the form

$$\int_0^V \left[\frac{1}{x} - \frac{1}{V}\right] a(x)\, dx = \psi(V) - \int_0^V [\psi(x) - \psi(V)]\, a(x)\, dx, \tag{8}$$

[†] To invoke the hypothesis of equal delay, we need only omit x from the denominator of the definition of $a(x)$.

or, integrating by parts on each side of Eq. (8),

$$\psi(V) + \int_0^V A(x)\, \psi'(x)\, dx = \int_0^V A(x)\, x^{-2}\, dx, \qquad (9)$$

which is satisfied by the following relationship between A and ψ:

$$\psi'(x)\, [1 + A(x)] = \frac{A(x)}{x^2}. \qquad (10)$$

Therefore ψ can be written explicitly in terms of A:

$$\psi(V) = \int_0^V \frac{A(x)}{1 + A(x)} \frac{dx}{x^2} \qquad (11)$$

and $m(x)$ can be obtained from $f_0(x)$ by means of Eqs. (7) and (11).

However, the transformation is not easy to perform in either direction. For example, the conjectured average speed given by Eq. (2) of Section 3.3 yields

$$\phi(V) = [\log \lambda'\, U\, e^V]^{-1} \qquad (12)$$

where U is defined by

$$U^{-1} = \lambda'\, e^V + \lambda' - \lambda. \qquad (13)$$

From this we obtain

$$\frac{1}{V^2} \frac{A(V)}{1 + A(V)} = V^{-2} - [\log \lambda'\, U\, e^V]^{-2}\, (\lambda' - \lambda)\, U; \qquad (14)$$

hence

$$A(V) = V^{-2}\, U^{-1}(\lambda' - \lambda)^{-1}\, [\log \lambda'\, e^V\, U]^2 - 1. \qquad (15)$$

Differentiating, we find the free speed distribution

$$f_0(V) \qquad (16)$$

$$= \frac{(1 - \lambda \Delta)\, [2V \log(\lambda'\, U\, e^V)\, (1 - \lambda'\, U\, e^V) - (\log \lambda'\, U\, e^V)^2\, (2 - \lambda'\, U V\, e^V)]}{k\, \rho\, (\lambda' - \lambda)\, V^2\, U}.$$

On the other hand, a Type III distribution with parameters p and q for free speeds leads to

$$A(V) = \frac{\rho\, k\, p}{1 - \lambda\Delta} \frac{\gamma(q-1, pV)}{\Gamma(q)},\tag{17}$$

and Eq. (11) cannot be explicitly evaluated. However, we note that the corresponding value for the Hypothesis of Equal Delay is

$$A(V) = \frac{\rho\, k\, p}{1 - \lambda\Delta} \frac{\gamma(q, pV)}{\Gamma(q)}.\tag{18}$$

Therefore a whole sequence of similarly plausible hypotheses can be constructed by changing the number of convolutions in the free speed density function.

In the argument leading to Eq. (11), there was one approximation involved, which the reader may have noticed. Equations (3) and (4) were formed by averaging over the supposed speed distribution of the free speed X of the car being followed, and as a matter of fact we assumed this distribution to be $f_0(x)$. However, in Section 7.2, we went to some trouble to show that the density function for the free speed of a car overtaken by a car of free speed V is

$$C(V)\,(V - x)\,\beta(x), \qquad 0 < x < V,\tag{19}$$

using the abbreviations C and β as defined in Section 7.3. This distribution, with Carleson's Hypothesis, leads to the equation[†]

$$V - m(V) = \frac{\rho\, k\, V}{1 - \lambda\Delta} \frac{\displaystyle\int_0^V \frac{V m(V) - m(x)}{m(x)} \frac{V - x}{x} \beta(x)\, dx}{\displaystyle\int_0^V (V - x)\,\beta(x)\, dx}.\tag{20}$$

[†] The integrals are Riemann-Liouville fractional integrals; cf. A. Erdelyi (ed.), "Tables of Integral Transforms," Vol. 2, Section 13.1. McGraw-Hill, New York, 1954.

And we have not yet found an explicit equation for $m(x)$! For $\beta(x)$ involves $\alpha(x)$, and this function, by Eqs. (2) and (3), itself depends on $m(x)$.

The results in the present section have been based mainly on Carleson's Hypothesis, which, as we have seen, does not differ substantially from the Hypothesis of Equal Delay. It appears that these conjectures will not easily be replaced by exactly derived formulas. Meanwhile, it is possible, and might be an improvement, to use formula (20) of Section 7.5 as a hypothesis, since this expression is exact in the isoveloxic case.

Although the emphasis in this section, as in the entire chapter, has been on mean values, in particular $m(V)$, it is important to note that Eqs. (2)–(5) can be replaced by distribution theoretic results. Since the test car passes, on the average $\rho(V, u)\, f_0(u)$ vehicles with speed in the range $(u, u + du)$ in unit time, we can write the function $h(u|V)$, defined in Section 7.2, Eq. (1), in the form

$$h(u|V)\, \rho(V, u)\, f_0(u)\, W. \tag{21}$$

Therefore

$$g(u|V) = \delta(u - V) \left[1 - \int_0^V \rho(V, v)\, W\, f_0(v)\, dv \right] + \rho(V, u)\, f_0(u)\, W \tag{22}$$

and

$$g(u) = f_0(u) - f_0(u) \int_0^u \rho(u, v)\, W\, f_0(v)\, dv + f_0(u) \int_u^\infty \rho(v, u)\, W\, f_0(v)\, dv. \tag{23}$$

In Eqs. (21)–(23) the arguments[†] of W are precisely the same as

---

[†] That is, the arguments relating to the speed of the vehicle being passed and of the vehicle passing; we are not now dealing with the parameters of the southbound stream.

those of ρ. Integrating out u from Eq. (23), we obtain an interesting relationship for the function

$$R(v, u) = \rho(v, u)\, W(v, u), \qquad v > u,$$

namely

$$\int_0^\infty \int_0^u R(u, v)\, f_0(u)\, f_0(v)\, dv\, du = \int_0^\infty \int_u^\infty R(v, u)\, f_0(u)\, f_0(v)\, dv\, du. \qquad (24)$$

7.7 Queueing Model

We will now discuss some of the difficulties involved in applying the differential-difference equation technique of Section 2.3 to the two lane road problem. The basic trouble is in deciding what quantities shall take the place of the probabilities $p_n(t)$. It is clearly nonsense to speak of *the* queue having n members at time t, for we have a multitude of queues. Moreover, it is not obvious how to isolate a single one of these queues for study, without a rule for saying which queue remains "the queue" when two queues coalesce at an overtaking or parturate at a passing. Instead we shall define

$$\lambda_n(t) = \text{Density of queues of } n \text{ at time } t.$$

Since

$$\sum_{n=1}^\infty n\, \lambda_n(t) = \lambda, \qquad (1)$$

the quantity

$$p_n(t) = (n/\lambda)\, \lambda_n(t), \qquad n = 1, 2, \ldots \qquad (2)$$

is an honest probability distribution characterizing the system. We then interpret $p_n(t)$ as the probability that an arbitrarily chosen car (the test car) belongs to a queue of n at time t.

The events which effect the length of the queue containing the test car are of four sorts: (i) test-car passes, (ii) another car passes, (iii) test queue overtakes another queue, (iv) test queue is overtaken by another queue.

We can compute the probabilities of these events in terms of formulas previously obtained. We begin with a simple case. Suppose the test car is travelling at its free speed, V. What is its probability of overtaking a car (or queue) in time Δt?[†] To overtake, there must have been a car with free speed $U < V$ within a distance $(V - U) \Delta t$, where U has the distribution of the next car overtaken, Eq. (19) of Section 7.2. Since the over-all density of vehicles is λ, the required probability can be written[‡]

$$\frac{\int_0^V (V - x)^2 \beta(x)\, dx}{\int_0^V (V - x)\, \beta(x)\, dx} \; \lambda\, \Delta t. \tag{3}$$

A very similar expression can be derived for the probability of the test queue being overtaken. In fact, defining

$$\Omega = \Omega(V) = \frac{\int_V^\infty (x - V)^2 \beta(x)\, dx}{\int_V^\infty (x - V)\, \beta(x)\, dx} + \frac{\int_0^V (V - x)^2 \beta(x)\, dx}{\int_0^V (V - x)\, \beta(x)\, dx} \tag{4}$$

we can write the probability of a run-on (overtaking or being overtaken) in time Δt by a car traveling at speed V in the form

$$\text{Prob (run-on}|V) = \lambda\, \Delta t\, \Omega(V). \tag{5}$$

Similarly, the probability of a run-on by a queue of i cars in time $(t, t + \Delta t)$ is

$$\text{Prob }(i\text{ run-on}|V) = \lambda_i(t)\, \Omega(V)\, \Delta t. \tag{6}$$

Equation (6) provides the means for computing probabilities needed for events (iii) and (iv) which effect the length of the queue in which the test car is found. In case the test car is not traveling

---

[†] Δ is no longer an augmented car length in this section.
[‡] Omitting, as throughout this argument, $o(\Delta t)$ terms.

at its free speed, the value V in Eq. (6) will need to be replaced by the traveling speed of the test car.

Next we shall consider transitions due to passing. If the test car is a queue by itself, there can be no passing; if there are two in queue, a passing reduces the number to one, whether it is the test car or the other car which passes. But for a queue of three or more, a passing by the test car reduces the number in its queue to one, while a passing by some other car reduces the queue length only from n to $(n-1)$. In this case, therefore, it is not possible to compute the effect of an opportunity to pass unless we also know which car takes advantage of the opportunity. There seems to be little loss in generality in assuming that cars pass only from the second position in the queue, so that the question is now reduced to finding whether the test car is in the second position. Notice that the effect of an opportunity to pass is the same if the test car is leading the queue as it is if the test car is in position 3, 4, ... Partly in ignorance and partly out of conviction, we shall assume that the test car is equally likely to occupy any position in the queue. Then an opportunity to pass presented to a test queue of n reduces the queue to $(n-1)$ with probability $(n-1)/n$ and reduces the queue to one with probability $(1/n)$.

The probability that an opportunity to pass occurs in time Δt can be written

$$\frac{A}{A+B}\Delta t$$

where A and B are defined in terms of the traveling speed of the test car and the properties of the southbound stream by Eqs. (8) and (9) of Section 5.5 and Eqs. (14) and (15) of Section 7.5. We can now form the differential-difference equation for the case $n > 1$. Bearing in mind Eqs. (2) and (5) of this section, we obtain

$$\frac{\partial p_n}{\partial t} = -\left(\frac{A}{A+B} + \lambda\Omega\right)p_n(t) + \tag{7}$$

$$\frac{n}{n+1}\frac{A}{A+B}p_{n+1}(t) + \lambda\Omega\sum_{i=1}^{n-1}\frac{1}{i}p_{n-i}(t)p_i(t).$$

When $n = 1$, the only complication arises from the exceptional case of two in a queue, where any opportunity to pass yields a $2 \to 1$ transition. Therefore

$$\frac{\partial p_1}{\partial t} = -\lambda \Omega p_1(t) + \frac{A}{A+B} p_2(t) + \sum_{i=3}^{\infty} \frac{A}{A+B} \frac{1}{i} p_i(t). \qquad (8)$$

The set of equations (7) and (8) connect the probabilities $p_n(t)$ with each other in a very unpleasant way, and the reader may well be appalled at the idea of seeking a solution. To deter any who may be optimistic, we point out that the equations need also to be averaged over the distribution of traveling speed of a car of free speed V, for example, Eq. (1), Section 7.2.

It is additionally lamentable to realize that, although this model[†] expresses properties of the northbound stream directly in terms of assumed properties of the southbound stream, rather than in terms of statistical conjectures about passing, nothing has yet been done to express properties of the southbound stream in terms of those of the northbound. The statistical equilibrium obtained through interaction between the two streams has not been even vaguely formulated.

7.8 Comment

The student of the two-lane model may well wish to begin with the exact geometry and dynamics of the passing maneuver. Kometani [5], Smirnov [14] and Tanner [18] deal fully with this question. Section 7.4 is based on Oliver's paper [11], in which three separate proofs[‡] are given for Eq. (3). Section 7.5, up to Eq. (5) is taken directly from a paper of Tanner [15]; from this point onwards we have very much simplified the treatment. The model is treated further by Tanner [16], 17]. The Hypothesis of Equal Delay is due to Haight [4].

[†] As well as the model presented in Section 7.4 from Eq. (10) onwards.
[‡] One of which Oliver attributes to Bisbee.

Section 7.6 deals with the traffic model of Carleson [3] and Andersson [1].

Miller [6, 8] gives an elaborate queueing model in which time, position and velocity are treated as jointly varying quantities. We have preferred to use a much easier system. Miller [7] also discusses very nicely some of the practical questions involved in the use of queueing models, and includes a treatment of the simple delay problem for a main road containing traffic queues.

Petigny [12] and Schuhl [13] discuss all these questions at great length, both from a theoretical and practical point of view. Kometani [5] and Petigny [12] also deal with the three lane road. (The definition of 'opportunity to pass' for a three lane road must be game-theoretic rather than deterministic. Hence, presumably, the deadly reputation of three lane roads.)

Mori [9, 10] ingeniously relates the opportunity to pass with a parameter characterizing the road. He assumes that the probability of passing a car of free speed V in a car of free speed U (in unit time) should be proportional to

$$\exp - V(U - V) \tag{1}$$

and calls the coefficient of proportionality the "road constant." His proposal certainly lends itself to numerical evaluation, and would also be valid if the conjecture (1) were replaced by some other expression.

Bartlett's difficult paper [2] also apparently deals with the subject of the present chapter. Many of the ideas presented here first appeared in primitive form in a paper by Newell [10 a].

REFERENCES

1. Andersson, B., Carlesons Trafikmodell (unpublished).
2. Bartlett, M. S., Some Problems Associated with Random Velocities. *Publ. Inst. Statist. Université Paris* **6**, No. 4, 261–270 (1957).
3. Carleson, L., En Matematisk Modell for Landsvägstrafik. *Nord. Matematisk Tidskrift* **5**, 176–180 (1957).
4. Haight, F. A., Towards a Unified Theory of Road Traffic. *Operations Research* **6**, No. 6, 813–826 (Nov.-Dec. 1958).

5. Kometani, E., On the Theoretical Solution of Highway Traffic Capacity Under Mixed Traffic. *Mem. Fac. Eng. Kyoto Univ.* **17**, 79–88 (1955).
6. Miller, A. J., Traffic Flow Treated as a Stochastic Process. *In Herman*, R. (ed.), "Theory of Traffic Flow," pp. 165–74. Proceedings of the Symposium on the Theory of Traffic Flow, held at the General Motors Research Laboratories, Warren, Michigan. Elsevier, Amsterdam, 1961.
7. Miller, A. J., A Queueing Model for Road Traffic Flow. *J. Roy. Statist. Soc.* Ser. B, **23**, No. 1, 64–90 (1961).
8. Miller, A. J., Road Traffic Considered as a Stochastic Process. *Proc. Cambridge Phil. Soc.* **58**, Part 2, 312–25 (1962).
9. Mori, M., Traffic Characteristics of Roads under Mixed Traffic Conditions. *Traffic Eng.* 23–28 (Oct. 1959).
10. Mori, M., On the Road Constant Indicating the Passing Characteristics of Roads under Mixed Traffic Conditions. *Mem. Fac. Eng. Osaka City Univ.* **2**, 9–18 (Dec. 1960).
10a. Newell, G. F., Mathematical Models for Freely-Flowing Highway Traffic. *Operations Research* **3**, No. 2, 176–186 (May 1955).
11. Oliver, R. M., Zero-One Bunching and a Passing Rule. Research Report No. 16. Operations Research Center, Univ. of California, Berkeley, California, July 25, 1961.
11a. Oliver, R. M., A note on Traffic Counting Distribution. *Operational Research Quarterly* **13**, No. 2, 171–8 (1962).
12. Petigny, B., Le calcul des probabilites et la circulation des véhicules sur les chaussées a deux ou trois voies. *Ann. Ponts et Chaussées* **131**, No. 2, 145–223 (March-April 1961).
13. Schuhl, A., Le calcul des probabilites et la circulation des vehicules sur une chaussé a deux voies. *Ann. Ponts et Chaussées* **125**, 631–663 (1955).
14. Smirnov, M., Fundamental Conditions for Safety in Passing. *The Organization and Safety of Traffic* (1960?) (In Russian.)
15. Tanner, J. C., A Simplified Model for Delays in Overtaking on a Two-Lane Road. *J. Roy. Statist. Soc.* Ser. B, **20**, No. 2, 408–414 (1958).
16. Tanner, J. C., An Improved Model for Delays on a Two Lane Road. Road Research Laboratory Research Note RN/3521/JCT (1959).
17. Tanner, J. C., An Improved Model for Delays on a Two Lane Road: Some Numerical Calculations. Road Research Laboratory Research Note RN/3777/JCT (1960).
18. Tanner, J. C., Delays on a Two-Lane Road. *J. Roy. Statist. Soc.* Ser. B, **23**, No. 1, 38–63 (1961).

Supplementary References

Abraham, C., La Répartition du Trafic Entre Itinéraires Concurrents. *Rev. gén. Routes et Aérodromes* **357**, 57–76 (Oct. 1961).

Alexandre, R., and Gardies, M., Aspects de la Circulation Routière dans la Région Parisienne. *Travaux Publics et Entreprises* **19**, 18–24 (Feb. 1960).

Anderson, R. L., Herman, R., and Prigogine, I., On the Statistical Distribution Function Theory of Traffic Flow. *Operations Research* **10**, No. 2, 180–96 (1962).

Berry, D. S., and Belmont, D. M., Distribution of Vehicle Speeds and Travel Times. "Proceedings of the Second Berkeley Symposium on Mathematical Statistics and Probability," pp. 589–602. Univ. of California Press, Berkeley, 1951.

Bideau, E., Les Aménagements Routiers dans la Banlieue Parisienne. *Travaux Publics et Entreprises* **23** (Sept. 1960).

Bideau, E., Circulation Routière et Transports Publics dans l'Agglomeration Parisienne. Section Danoise de la Société des Ingénieurs Civils de France Copenhagen, Jan. 1962.

Bidwell, J. B., The Car-Road Complex. *In* "Theory of Traffic Flow," Proceedings of the Symposium on the Theory of Traffic Flow, held at the General Motors Research Labs., Warren, Michigan (R. Herman, ed.), pp. 1–9. Elsevier, Amsterdam, 1961.

Billinger, H., Untersuchungen zur Vereinfachung von Querschnittszählungen des Straßenverkehrs. *Strasse u. Autobahn* **12**, Part 3, 101–9 (1961).

Brenner, R., Mathewson, J. H., and Gerlough, D. L., A General Method for Estimating Through Traffic in a Road Network. *Highway Research Abstr.* **27**, No. 8, 32–48 (1957).

Brenner, R., Telford, E. T., and Frischer, D., A Quantitative Evaluation of Traffic in a Complex Freeway Network. Paper presented at the 40th Annual Meeting of the Highway Research Board, Washington D. C., Jan. 1961.

Buckley, D. J., Road Traffic Headway Distributions. Paper presented at the First Biennial Conference of the Australian Road Research Board, Sept. 10–14, 1962.

Charlesworth, G., Road and Traffic Research. *In* "Roads and Their Traffic," pp. 255–80. Blackie & Son, London, 1960.

Charnes, A., and Cooper, W. W., Extremal Principles for Simulating Traffic Flows in a Network. *Proc. Natl. Acad. Sci. U. S.* **44**, No. 2, 201–4 (1958).

Charnes, A., and Cooper, W. W., Multicopy Traffic Network Models. *In* "Theory of Traffic Flow," Proceedings of the Symposium on the Theory of Traffic Flow held at the General Motors Research Labs., Warren, Michigan (R. Herman, ed.), pp. 85–96. Elsevier, Amsterdam, 1961.

Clayton, A. J. H., Road Traffic Calculations. *J. Inst. Civil Engrs.* **16**, No. 7, 247–284 (1941); No. 8, 588–594 (1941).

Clissold, C. M., "The Distribution of Acceptance Gaps for Crossing and Turning Manoeuvres," Thesis, M. Tech. School of Traffic Eng., Univ. of New South Wales, Australia, 1960.

Cohen, J. W., A Lecture on Stochastic Processes in Road Traffic. Tech. Univ. Delft, May 1962 (in Dutch). To appear in *De Ingenieur* (1963).

Cohen, J. W., A Note on the Delay Problem in Crossing a Traffic Stream. Math. Inst. der Tech. Hogeschool Delft, May 1962. To appear in *Statistica Neerlandica* (1963).

Crawford, A., and Taylor, D. H., Driver Behaviour at Traffic Lights, Critical Amber Period. *Traffic Eng. and Control* **3**, No. 8, 473–78, 482 (1961).

Dorfwirth, J. R., Wartezeit und Rückstau von Kraftfahrzeugen an nicht signalgeregelten Verkehrsknoten. *Forschungsarb. Strassenwesen* **43** (1961).

Dorfwirth, J. R., and Handler, H., Verkehrsplanung und Mathematik, IV. Ergebnis der Analyse des individuellen Verkehrs an Gebiets- und Netzmodellen. *Math. Tech. Wirtschaft* **8**, Part 2, 57–62 (1961).

Durand-Dubief, M., Les Besoins de Transport dans l'Agglomeration Parisienne. *Travaux Publics et Entreprises* **19**, 11–17 (Feb. 1960).

Edie, L. C., Expectancy of Multiple Vehicular Breakdowns in a Tunnel. *Operations Research* **3**, No. 4, 513–522 (1955). Discussion and author's closure, *Ibid.* **4**, No. 5, 609–619 (1956).

Egert, P., "The Mathematical Principles of Traffic Statistics," Tech. und Volkswirt. Berichte des Wirtschafts- und Verkehrsministerium, Nordrhein-Westfalen, 1954.

Egert, P., Strassenverkehr als Aufgabe theoretischer Grundlagenforschung. *Strasse u. Autobahn* **13**, Part 5, 185–91 (1962).

Engel, E., Zur Frage der praktischen Leistungsfähigkeit signalisierter Knotenpunkte des Strassenverkehrs. *Strasse u. Autobahn* **10**, Part 6, 223–228 (1959).

Engel, E., Ein Verfahren zur Fahrzeitermittlung von Kraftfahrzeugen. *Strasse u. Autobahn* **13**, Part 2, 69–70 (1962).

Engel, E., and Meissl, P., Fahrzeugstau und Wartezeiten an Signalen, II. *Strasse u. Autobahn* **5**, Part 3, 110–113 (1961).

Fischer, R., Leistung von Kreuzungen im gemischten Stadtverkehr. *Strasse u. Autobahn* **9**, Part 9, 339–346 (1958).

Gazis, D., Herman, R., and Maradudin, A., The Problem of the Amber Signal Light in Traffic Flow. *Operations Research* **8**, No. 1, 112–132 (1960). Reprinted in *Traffic Eng.* **30**, No. 10, 19–26 and 53 (1960).

Gerlough, D. L., and Mathewson, J. H., Approaches to Operational Problems in Street and Highway Traffic. *Operations Research* **4**, No. 1, 32–41 (1956).

Gerlough, D. L., Some Problems in Intersection Traffic Control. *In* "Theory of Traffic Flow," Proceedings of the Symposium on the Theory of Traffic Flow, held at the General Motors Research Labs., Warren, Michigan (R. Herman, ed.), pp. 10–27. Elsevier, Amsterdam, 1961.

Gluss, B., Four Streams of Traffic Converging on a Cross-Road. (Abstract.) *Ann. Math. Statist.* **27**, 215–6 (1956).

Goebel, K., Parkraumbedarf und Belastungskennziffern des ruhenden Verkehrs in den Kernen westdeutscher Großstädte. *Strasse u. Autobahn* **11**, Part 1, 31–42 (1960).

Goode, H. H., The Application of a High Speed Computer to the Definition and Solution of the Vehicular Traffic Problem. *Operations Research* **5**, No. 6, 775–93 (1957).

Goode, H. H., Pollmar, C. H., and Wright, J. B., The Use of a Digital Computer to Model a Signalized Intersection. *Proc. Highway Research Board* **35**, 548–557 (1956).

Grassmann, R., and Steierwald, G., Geschwindigkeitsablauf und Überholvorgänge auf zweispurigen Richtungsfahrbahnen. *Strasse u. Autobahn* **10**, Part 8, 291–296 (1959).

Greenberg, I., "A Vehicle Headway Distribution for Tunnels." Port of New York Authority. (Unpublished.)

Greenshields, B. D., Shapiro, D., and Ericksen, E. L., Traffic Performance at Urban Street Intersections. Technical Report No. 1, pp. 73–109, Yale Bureau of Highway Traffic, 1947.

Gunnarsson, O., Trafikflödesberäkningar — ett Databehandlingsproblem. *Svenska Vägföreningens Tidskr.* **4**, 1–8 (1960).

Gunnarsson, O., Optimal Linjesträckning av Trafikleder. (English summary.) *Teknisk Tidskr., Uppl. D*, pp. 1–5 (24 June 1960).

Haight, F. A., and Mosher, W. W., A Practical Method for Improving the Accuracy of Vehicular Speed Distribution Measurements. *Highway Research Board Bull.* **341** (1962).

Hankin, B. D., and Wright, R. A., Passenger Flow in Subways. *Operational Research Quarterly* **9**, No. 2, 81–88 (1958).

Helly, W., Simulation of Bottlenecks in Single-Lane Traffic Flow. *In* "Theory of Traffic Flow," Proceedings of the Symposium on the Theory of Traffic Flow, held at the General Motors Research Labs., Warren, Michigan (R. Herman, ed.), pp. 207–38. Elsevier, Amsterdam, 1961.

Helm, B., Saturation Flow of Traffic at Light Controlled Intersections. *Traffic Eng.* **32**, No. 5, 22–27 (1962).

Herman, R., Mathematical Theory of Traffic Flow. *Proc. Inst. Traffic Engrs.* **30**, 67–79 (1960).

Herwald, N., Some Theoretical Aspects of Control of Road Traffic. *J. Sci. Instruments* **14**, No. 12, 393–401 (1937).

Hoffman, W., and Pavely, R., Applications of Digital Computers to Problems in the Study of Vehicular Traffic. *Proc. Western Joint Computer Conf.*, pp. 159–161 (1958).

Hoffman, W., and Pavely, R., Method for Solution of the Nth Best Path. *J. Assoc. Computing Machinery* **6**, No. 4, 506–14 (1959).

Hondermarcq, E., Instantaneous Traffic Volumes. *In* "Traffic Characteristics: Their Variation and Prediction," Theme I, pp. 20–25. International Study Week in Traffic Engineering, Bürgenstock, Switzerland, Sept. 1954.

Inzinger, R., Verkehrsplanung und Mathematik, II. Das mathematische Modell einer Verkehrserhebung. *Math. Tech. Wirtschaft* **7**, 107–9 (1960).

Jensen, A., Traffic Theory as an Aid in the Planning and Operation of the Road Grid. *Ingeniøren* (*Intern. Ed.*) **1**, No. 2, 48–61 (1957).

Jewell, W. S., Multiple Entries in Traffic. Research Report No. 29, Operations Research Center, Univ. of California, Berkeley, July 1962.

Kell, J. H., Analyzing Vehicular Delay at Intersections Through Simulation. *Highway Research Board Bull.* **356** (1962).

Kinzer, J. P., "Application of the Theory of Probability to Problems of Highway Traffic," B.C.E. Thesis. Polytech. Inst. of Brooklyn, 1933; Abstract in *Proc. Inst. Traffic Engrs.* **5**, 118–124 (1934).

Knödel, W., Verkehrsplanung und Mathematik, III. Netzmodelle. *Math. Tech. Wirtschaft* **7**, 147–54 (1960).

Knoll, E., Beitrag zur Berechnung signalgesteuerter Strassenknoten. *Strasse u. Autobahn* **10**, Part 11, 443–451 (1959).

Kometani, E., and Sasaki, T., A Safety Index for Traffic with Linear Spacing. *Operations Research* **7**, No. 6, 704–20 (1959).

Korte, J. W., and Leutzbach, W., Zeitlückenverteilung bei gestörten Verkehrsströmen. *Verkehr u. Technik* **9**, Part 1, 17–18 (1956).

Korte, J. W., and Mäcke, P., Der Überholungsvorgang auf zweispurigen Strassen mit Gegenverkehr. *Strasse u. Autobahn* **7**, No. 8, 280–3; No. 11, 400–3 (1960).

Korte, J. W., Mäcke, P. A., and Kirsch, H., Anzahl der Merkmale bei Verkehrszählungen — eine Variationsbetrachtung. *Strasse u. Autobahn* **10**, Part 10, 393–399 (1959).

Korte, J. W., Mäcke, P. A., and Lapierre, R., Gestaltung von Strassenverkehrsanlagen, I. Kreuzungsanlagen. *Forschungsber. d. Landes Nordrhein-Westfalen* **610** (1959).

Krell, K., Theorie der Zeitlücken von Strassenverkehrsströmen. *Strasse u. Autobahn* **9**, Part 3, 167–70 (1958).

Krell, K., Ermittlung der Leistung ungesteuerter Strassenknoten mit Hilfe der Zeitlückentheorie. *Strasse u. Autobahn* **9**, Part 8, 293–97 (1958).

Krell, K., Experimentelle Methoden in der Strassenverkehrstechnik. *Strasse u. Autobahn* **10**, Part 2, 71–75 (1959).

Kremser, H., Ein einfaches Wartzeitproblem bei einem Poissonschen Verkehrsfluss. *Österr. Ing.-Arch.* **16**, No. 1, 75–90 (1961).

Kremser, H., Ein zusammengesetztes Wartzeitproblem bei Poissonschen Verkehrsströmen. *Österr. Ing.-Arch.* **16**, No. 3, 231–52 (1962).

Krylov, Yu. S., Traffic Movement and Road Capacity. *Avtom. Dorogi* **22**, No. 6, 16–18 (1959).

Lefevre, P., "Experimental Study on the Capacity of Two-Lane Roads," Theme II. Fifth International Study Week in Traffic Engineering, Nice, France, Sept. 1960.

Leutzbach, W., "Ein Beitrag zur Zeitlückenverteilung gestörter Strassenverkehrsströme," Dissertation. Tech. Hochschule Aachen, 1956.

Leutzbach, W., Zeitlückenverteilungen. *Strasse u. Autobahn* **8**, Part 1, 17–20 (1957).

Leutzbach, W., Graphisches Hilfsmittel zur Berechnung von Signalanlagen. *Strasse u. Autobahn* **9**, Part 5, 189–92 (1958).

Leutzbach, W., Verkehrsmenge, Verkehrsdichte und Geschwindigkeit. *Strasse u. Autobahn* **13**, Part 4, 151–56 (1962).

Leutzbach, W., and Egert, P., Geschwindigkeitsmessungen vom fahrenden Fahrzeug aus. *Strasse u. Autobahn* **10**, Part 3, 23–28 (1959).

Leutzbach, W., and Egert, P., Geschwindigkeiten im Strassenverkehr ausserhalb geschlossener Ortslagen, I und II. Auftrag des Ministeriums für Wirtschaft und Verkehr, Nordrhein-Westfalen, 1959.

Leutzbach, W., and Egert, P., Geschwindigkeiten im Strassenverkehr ausserhalb geschlossener Ortschaften. *Strasse u. Autobahn* **11**, Part 8, 360–363 (1960).

Lighthill, M. J., Dynamic Instability of Transport Systems: The Hydrodynamic Analogy. *Operational Research Quarterly* **8**, No. 3, 109–114 (1957).

Linckh, A., Anwendung des Wahrscheinlichkeitsnetzes für die Analyse von Verkehrsspitzen im Strassenverkehr. *Strasse u. Autobahn* **11**, No. 4, 182–4 (1960).

Major, N. G., and Buckley, D. J., Entry to a Traffic Stream. Paper presented at the First Biennial Conference of the Australian Road Research Board, Sept 10–14, 1962.

Malcor, R., Theory of Road Traffic and Operational Research. *Travaux* **42**, No. 280, 137–42 (1958).

Mathewson, J. H., Trautman, D. L., and Gerlough, D. L., Study of Traffic Flow by Simulation. *Proc. Highway Research Board* **34**, 522–30 (1955).

May, A. D., Jr., and Wagner, F. A., Headway Characteristics and Inter-relationships of the Fundamental Characteristics of Traffic Flow. *Proc. Highway Research Board* **39**, 524–47 (1960).

Meissl, P., Stochastisches Modell einer festzeitgesteuerten Rot-Grün-Signalanlage, I. *Math. Tech. Wirtschaft* **9**, No. 1, 11–18 (1962).

Meissl, P., Stochastisches Modell einer festzeitgesteuerten Rot-Grün-Signalanlage, II. *Math. Tech. Wirtschaft* **9**, No. 2, 65–69 (1962).

Michaels, R. M., and Solomon, D., The Effect of Speed Change Information on Spacing Between Vehicles. *Public Roads* **31**, No. 12, 229–35 (1962).

Miller, A. J., An Analysis of Bunching in Rural Two-Lane Traffic. *Operations Research* (to appear).

Montroll, E. W., Acceleration Noise and Clustering Tendency of Vehicular Traffic. *In* "The Theory of Traffic Flow," Proceedings of the Symposium on the Theory of Traffic Flow, held at the General Motors Research Labs., Warren, Michigan (R. Herman, ed.), pp. 147–57. Elsevier, Amsterdam, 1961.

Morgan, J. T., "The Unsignalised Intersection in Poisson Traffic." Canberra, Australia, 1962. (Unpublished manuscript.)

Murànyi, T., Anwendung einer neuen Methode der Verkehrsforschung bei Landeserhebungen. *Strasse u. Autobahn* **9**, Part 3, 119–26 (1958).

Murànyi, T., Scientific Foundations of Highway System Planning. *Acta Tech. Acad. Sci. Hungary* **16**, 13 (1956).

Newell, G. F., "Synchronization of Traffic Lights for High Flow." (Unpublished mimeograph.)

Nordqvist, S., Gàtors och Vägors Kapacitet. Communication No. 39, IVA Transportforskningskommission, Stockholm, 1960.

Oliver, R. M., Travel Times Through Shock Waves. Research Report No. 17, Operations Research Center, Univ. of California, Berkeley, July 1962.

Oliver, R. M., Delays to Aircraft Serviced by the Glide Path. *Operational Research Quarterly* **13**, No. 2, 201–9 (1962).

Oliver, R. M., Bisbee, E. F., Pestalozzi, G., Dysli, J.-C., Vehicle Queues in Mixed Traffic Streams, Progress Report. Research Report No. 35, Inst. of Transportation and Traffic Eng., Univ. of California, Berkeley, Oct. 1962.

Oliver, R. M., "Delays in Terminal Air Traffic Control." (Unpublished mimeograph.)

Oliver, R. M., Bisbee, E. F., and Pestalozzi, G., Vehicle Space-Occupancy in Moving Streams of Traffic. Research Report No. 34, Inst. of Transportation and Traffic Eng. Univ. of California, Berkeley, July 1962.

Oliver, R. M., and Newman, L., Effect of Trucks on Freeway Flows. Paper for presentation at the 42nd Annual Meeting of the Highway Research Board, Washington, D. C., Jan. 1963.

Pacey, G. M., "Some Problems in the Study of Road Traffic Flow," M.S. Thesis. Univ. of Manchester, England.

Pacey, G. M., The Progress of a Bunch of Vehicles Released from a Traffic Signal. Research Note RN/2665/GMP, Road Research Lab., Harmondsworth, Middlesex, England, Jan. 1956.

Palm, J., "Busshållplatsers Kapacitet," Thesis, Civil Eng. Royal Inst. of Technol., Stockholm, Sweden, 1962.

Pebereau, G., Les Transports Publics de Voyageurs dans la Région Parisienne. *Travaux Publics et Entreprises* **19**, 25–32 (Feb. 1960).

Peleg, M., Encounter of Vehicles at Intersections. *Bull. Research Council Israel* **C7**, No. 1, 55–60 (1959).

Perchonok, P. A., and Levy, S. L., Application of Digital Simulation Techniques to Freeway On-Ramp Traffic Operations. Final Report to Bureau of Public Roads, Midwest Research Inst., Kansas City, Missouri, Nov. 1959. *Proc. Highway Research Board* **39**, 506–23 (1960).

Prager, W., Problems in Traffic and Transportation. Proceedings of a Symposium on Operations Research in Business and Industry, Midwest Research Inst., Kansas City, Missouri, Apr. 1954.

Prager, W., On the Role of Congestion in Transportation Problems. *Z. angew. Math. u. Mech.* **35**, 264–8 (1955).

Prager, W., On the Design of Communication and Transportation Networks. *In* "Theory of Traffic Flow," Proceedings of the Symposium on the Theory of Traffic Flow held at the General Motors Research Labs., Warren, Michigan (R. Herman, ed.), pp. 97–104. Elsevier, Amsterdam, 1961.

Prigogine, I., A Boltzmann-Like Approach to the Statistical Theory of Traffic Flow. *In* "Theory of Traffic Flow," Proceedings of the Symposium on the Theory of Traffic Flow, held at the General Motors Research Labs., Warren, Michigan (R. Herman, ed.), pp. 158–64. Elsevier, Amsterdam, 1961.

Prigogine, I., and Andrews, F. C., A Boltzmann-Like Approach for Traffic Flow. *Operations Research* **8**, No. 6, 789–97 (1960).

Prigogine, I., On Individual and Collective Flow. *Bull. Cl. sci., acad. roy. Belg.* (to appear 1962).

Prigogine, I., and Résibois, P., On a Generalized Boltzmann-Like Approach for Traffic Flow. *Bull. Cl. sci., acad. roy. Belg.* (to appear 1962).

Rashevsky, N., Some Remarks on the Mathematical Aspects of Automobile Driving. *Bull. Math. Biophys.* **21**, 299–308 (1959).

Reynolds, D. J., and Wardrop, J. G., "Economic Losses due to Traffic Congestion." Theme III. Fifth International Study Week in Traffic Engineering, Nice, France, Sept. 1960.

Road Research Laboratory. "List of Publications on Traffic and Safety" (May 1961), Research Note RN/3987, a revision of RN/3774. Division: Traffic and Safety, Dept. of Scientific and Industrial Research.

Romanenko, I. A., The Design of Three-Way Junctions. *Avtom. Dorogi* **22**, No. 10, 19–22 (1959).

Scholz, G., Zur Analyse des Personenverkehrs in Grossstädten. *Strasse u. Autobahn* **9**, Part 11, 451–59 (1958).

Schramm, G., Wie hängt die Leistungsfähigkeit einer Strasse von der Fahrgeschwindigkeit ab? *Strasse u. Autobahn* **10**, Part 7, 261–2 (1959).

Schuhl, A., Le Calcul des Probabilités et la Répartition des Véhicules sur les Routes à Deux Voies de Circulation. *Travaux* **39**, No. 243, 16–18 (1955).

Scott, J. R., and Tanner, J. C., Traffic Trends and Vehicle-Miles in Great Britain, 1938–1960. *Surveyor, London* **121**, No. 3469, 645–8 (1962).

Shimel'fenig, S. A., Traffic Lane Capacity. *Avtom. Dorogi* **22**, No. 10, 31 (1959).

Shumate, R. P., and Crowther, R. F., Variability of Fixed-Point Speed Measurements. *Highway Research Board Bull.* **281**, 87–96 (1961).

Smeed, R. J., Traffic Flow. *Operational Research Quarterly* **8**, No. 3, 115–23, Discussion 142–8 (1957).

Smeed, R. J., Theoretical Studies and Operational Research on Traffic and Traffic Congestion. *Bull. inst. intern. statist.* **36**, Part 4, 347–75 (1958).

Smeed, R. J., "The Traffic Problem in Towns." Manchester Statist. Soc., Feb. 1961.

Stanley, A. L., "A Study of the Variables Involved and the Statistical Techniques Utilized in Conducting and Evaluating a Traffic Experiment on Traffic Delays at Overloaded Intersections," Ph.D. Dissertation. Univ. of California, Los Angeles, 1949.

Steierwald, G., "Traffic Operations on Roads with Dual Carriageways; a Contribution to Road Traffic Statistics," Dissertation. Tech. Hochschule Aachen, 1959.

von Stein, W., Traffic Flow with Pre-Signals and the Signal Funnel. *In* "Theory of Traffic Flow," Proceedings of the Symposium on the Theory of Traffic Flow, held at the General Motors Research Labs., Warren, Michigan (R. Herman, ed.), pp. 28–56. Elsevier, Amsterdam. 1961.

Sylvén, E., Trafikprognosmetod för Tätortsområden. *Teknisk Tidskr.* (Sept. 1960).

Tanner, J. C., Weather and Road Traffic Flow. *Weather* **7**, No. 9, 270–5 (1952).

Tanner, J. C., Effect of Weather on Traffic Flow. *Nature* **169**, No. 4290, 107 (1952).

Tanner, J. C., The Sampling of Road Traffic. *Appl. Statistics* **6**, No. 3, 161–70 (1957).

Tanner, J. C., A Theoretical Analysis of Delays at an Uncontrolled Intersection. Research Note RN/3937/JCT, Road Research Lab., Harmondsworth, Middlesex, England, Feb. 1961. *Biometrika* **49**, Parts 1 and 2, 163–70 (1962).

Turner, J. K., and Wardrop, J. G., The Variation of Journey Time in Central London. Research Note RN/1511/JKT.JGW, Road Research Lab., Harmondsworth, Middlesex, England, Feb. 1951.

Turner, J. K., and Wardrop, J. G., The Variation in the Time Stopped at Controlled Intersections in Central London. Research Note RN/2158/JKT.JGW, Road Research Lab., Harmondsworth, Middlesex, England, Feb. 1954.

Voorhees, A. M., A General Theory of Traffic Movement. *Proc. Inst. Traffic Engrs.* **25**, 46–56 (1955).

Vulis, D., Some Problems of Road Design. *Avtom. Dorogi* **24**, No. 12, 22–4 (1962).

Waagensen, B., Nogle Beliggenhedssporgsmaal i Planen. Communication No. 12, Den Polytekniske Laereanstalts, Laboratorium for vej og jernbanebygning, Copenhagen, 1945.

Wardrop, J. G., The Relation Between Speed and Flow in Central London. Research Report RN/1021/JGW, Road Research Lab., Harmondsworth, Middlesex, England.

Wardrop, J. G., Some Theoretical Aspects of Road Traffic Research. *Proc. Inst. Civil Engrs.*, Part II **1**, No. 2, 325–62, Discussion 362–78 (1952).

Wardrop, J. C., The Distribution of Traffic on a Road System. *In* "Theory of Traffic Flow," Proceedings of the Symposium on the Theory of Traffic Flow, held at the General Motors Research Labs., Warren, Michigan (R. Herman, ed.), pp. 57–78. Elsevier, Amsterdam, 1961.

Wardrop, J. G., and Charlesworth, G., A Method of Estimating Speed and Flow of Traffic from a Moving Vehicle. *J. Inst. Civil Engrs.*, Part II **3**, No. 1, 158–71 (1954).

Wardrop, J. G., and Duff, J. T., Factors Affecting Road Capacity. *Transportation and Communication Monthly Rev.* **174**, 22–27 (1961).

Watson, Henry, "Street Traffic Flow." Chapman & Hall, London, 1933.

Webster, F. V., "Traffic Signal Settings and Expected Delay." International Study Week in Traffic Engineering, Stresa, Italy, Oct. 1956.

Webster, F. V., Traffic Signal Settings. Tech. Paper No. 39, Road Research Lab., Harmondsworth, Middlesex, England, 1958.

Webster, F. V., and Wardrop, J. G., "Capacity of Urban Intersections," Theme II. Sixth International Study Week in Traffic Engineering, Salzburg, Austria, Sept. 1962.

Weiss, G., "An Analysis of Pedestrian Queueing." (To appear.)

Whiting, P. D., and Hillier, J. A., A Method for Finding the Shortest Route Through a Road Network. *Operational Research Quarterly* **11**, No. 1–2, 37–40 (1960).

Wong, S. Y., Traffic Simulator with a Digital Computer. *Proc. Western Joint Computer Conf.*, pp. 92–4 (Feb. 1956).

Yablonskii, S. V., Gilman, A. M., *et al.*, Cybernetics and Theory of Regulation; Device for Investigation of Algorisms of Street Traffic Control. *Doklady Akad. Nauk S.S.S.R.* **132**, No. 1, 78–81 (1960).

Yeo, G. F., and Weesakul, B., Distribution of Delay to Traffic at an Intersection. (Unpublished.)

Author Index

Numbers in parentheses are reference numbers and are included to assist in locating references when the authors' names are not mentioned in the text. Numbers in italics indicate the page on which the reference is listed.

A

Abraham, C., *227*
Adams, W. F., 162, *164*
Alexandre, R., *227*
Anderson, R. L., *227*
Andersson, B., 224, *224*
Andrews, F. C., *232*

B

Bailey, N. T. J., 163, *164*
Barnes, H. A., 89, *92*
Bartle, R. M., *164*
Bartlett, M. S., 131, *131*, 224, *224*
Beckmann, M. J., 163, *165*
Bellman, R. E., 63, *64*
Belmont, D. M., *227*
Berry, D. S., *165*, *227*
Bharucha-Reid, A. T., 63, *64*
Bick, J. H., 91, *92*
Bideau, E., *227*
Bidwell, J. B., *227*
Billinger, H., *227*
Bisbee, E. F., 164(26), *166*, 195(11), *196*, *196*, *197*, *232*
Bisi, W., 163, *165*
Borel, E., 64, *64*
Breiman, L., 130, *131*
Brenner, R., *227*
Breuer, M. A., 64, *65*
Brockmeyer, E., 62(4), 63(4), *65*, 195(2), *196*
Bromwich, T. J. I'a., 64, *65*
Buckley, D. J., *227*, *231*
Burke, P. J., 195, *196*

C

Carleson, L., 224, *224*
Castoldi, L., *165*
Chandler, R. E., *92*
Charlesworth, G., *227*, *234*
Charnes, A., *227*
Chow, Tse-Sun, 90, *92*
Clarke, A. B., 196, *196*
Clayton, A. J. H., *227*
Clissold, C. M., *228*
Cohen, J. W., 164, *165*, *228*
Cooper, W. W., *227*
Cox, D. R., 195, 196, *196*
Crawford, A., *228*
Creighton, R. L., 89, *92*
Crowther, R. F., 163, *165*, *233*

D

Daou, A., 91, *95*
De, S. C., 91, *93*
Dearnaley, E. J., 164(9), *165*
Doig, A., 63, *65*
Domb, C., 131, *131*
Dorfwirth, J. R., *228*
Duff, J. T., *234*
Durand-Dubief, M., *228*
Dysli, J.-C., *232*

E

Edie, L. C., 89, 91, *93*, 195, *197*, *228*
Egert, P., *228*, *231*
Engel, E., 164, *165*, *228*
Erdelyi, A., 32(1), *33*
Ericksen, E. L., *229*

235

Subject Index

A

Arithmetic mean, *see Mean*
Array distribution, 24
Asymptotic state probabilities, 37
Asynchronous counting, defined 97, 102,
    105, 110, 124, 139
Augmented car length, 107
Augmented unblock, 142

B

Balking, 62
Ballot problem, 64
Bayes Theorem, 24, 43, 98, 202
Bernoulli experiment, 8, 25, 112, 121
Beta distribution, 19
Beta function, 13
Binomial distribution, 7–8, 18–20, 161
Bivariate distribution, 1.8 (23)
Blackwell's Theorem, 124
Block, 142, 150
Borel distribution, 64, 113
Borel-Tanner distribution, defined 56
    Eq.(13), 64, 146 ff., 188, 191
Bottleneck, 6.8 (188)
Bulk service, 62, 5.9 (157), 163
Bunch, 111
Busy period, 36, 2.6 (53)

C

Capacity, 72, 73, 81, 84, 89
Car following, 3.4 (76), 3.8 (85), 89, 90
Carleson's Hypothesis, 207, 212, 216,
    218, 219
Cauchy distribution, 25
Certain experiment, 1, 21
Complex passing, 206
Compound passing, 206, 208
Concentration, 70, *see Density*
Conditional distribution, 24, 98, 128,
    139, 146, 155

Continuous distribution, 1.4 (9), 31
Convolution, 29, 30, 61, 101, 128
Correlation coefficient, 26
Counting distribution, 12, 30, 97, 100,
    pooled counting 174
Covariance, 26
Cumulative distribution, 1.6 (15), 22,
    27, 35

D

Delay, Chapter 5
Density function, 10
Density of traffic, 70, 84, 200, 215, 220
Deterministic distribution, 21, 37
Diminished block, 142
Discrete distribution, 1.2 (4), 31
Discrete time, 161
Distribution, *see* name of particular
    distribution
Domain of definition, 2, 10
Dummy variable, 4, 16

E

Efflux Traffic Queueing Model, 113, 209
Empirical distribution, 4
Equilibrium delay function, 123
Erlang's Loss Formula, 181, 182
Erlang process, Definition 60–1, Star-
    ting density 99, Counting distribu-
    tions 4.4 (103), 109, 178
Expectation, 1.7 (19), 59
Exponential acceleration, 186
Exponential probability generating
    function, 27

F

Factorial moments, 27, 105
Fair die, 5
Flow, 70, 162

239

199 ff., 205, 207, conditional distribution 116–117, 204, 206, also 120–122, 127
Starting density, 98
State of a queue, 37, 41
Statistical distribution, 1
Stochastic process, 2.1 (35), 97
Stop sign, 136
Stuttering Poisson distribution, 130
Synchronous counting, 97, 101, 107, 113, 139

T

Tail of a distribution, 22
Telephone traffic, 195
Traffic dynamics, 92, 176
Traffic intensity, 37
Traffic light, 37, 135–136, 144 ff., optimal phases 6.2 (167), sequences 6.5 (176)
Transient state, 37
Transition matrix, 48, 49, 157, 158, 169, 172, 189, 190
Translated distributions, 4.5 (107)
Translated negative exponential distribution, 108
Truncated negative exponential distribution, 108
Truncated Poisson distribution, 181
Type I Counter, 129
Type II Counter, 163
Type I distribution, 12, 13, 18, 19, 20, 75

Type III distribution, definition 10–11, cumulative distribution 18, mean and variance 20, Laplace transform 30, applications 43–44, 60–61, 75, 104, 116, 218

U

Unblock, 142, 150
Uncertain experiment, 1, 21
Unconditional distribution, 23, 137, 177
Unresponsive service, 136, 145

V

Variance, definition 20–21, bivariate 26, of speed 75, of waiting time in a queue 45, 193–194, of counting distribution 106, of waiting time to cross a road 141
Velocity, *see Speed*
Virtual waiting time, 36, 42 ff., 50, *see* also *Waiting time*
Volume, 70, *see* also *Flow*

W

Waiting time, 14, 36, 42–44, 49–53, 60

Y

Yield sign, 196

Z

Zero-One model, 7.4 (209)